148 Vermont St.
Roch. 9, N.Y.

'Work is Love made visible.'

THE WOOL MERCHANT OF SEGOVIA

St. Alphonsus Foretells to St. Peter Claver His Future Work

The Wool Merchant of Segovia

(St. Alphonsus Rodriguez)

MABEL FARNUM

THE BRUCE PUBLISHING COMPANY
Milwaukee

Br
R
Fa

Nihil obstat: H. B. Ries, Censor librorum
Imprimatur: ✠ Moyses E. Kiley, Archiepiscopus Milwaukiensis
Die 1 Junii, 1945

This book is produced in complete accord with the Government rules and regulations for the conservation of paper and other essential materials.

To Alfred
For his devotion to the Queen
and Saints of the Society
of Jesus.

Acknowledgments

FOR the data on the life of St. Alphonsus Rodriguez presented in this book the biography of the Saint by Father Francis Goldie, S.J., published in London in 1889, was used. From the many incidents recorded by Father Goldie, who gathered his material from the accounts of Fathers Nonell, Julian, Marimon, Colin and Don Furio y Sastre, various types were selected to illustrate the character and work of the famous Lay Brother of the Society of Jesus.

The conversations between the members of the Jesuit Communities identified with St. Alphonsus are authentic, and taken from the records. These conversations and the incidents chosen for presentation here have been woven into the history of the religious, social and economic structure of sixteenth century and early seventeenth century Spain. The descriptions of the old Spanish cities were derived from texts and sketches preserved in the Fine Arts Department of the Boston Public Library.

The form of the Saint's name, "Alonso," is used because this is the original Spanish name of the holy Brother, which he employed in his writings and by which he was known to his brethren. The title "Company of Jesus" is also used, because the Spanish form, "Campagnia" was that which St. Ignatius Loyola gave to his organization, and because the locale of this book is Spain. Also in Spain and elsewhere in those early centuries the scholastics of the Society of Jesus appear to have had the title "Brother" together with the temporal coadjutors, the lay brothers.

The author wishes to thank the Most Reverend Richard J.

Cushing, D.D., LL.D., Archbishop of Boston, a tireless missionary, for his constant and generous interest and assistance in promoting this work, as also the two Jesuit Mission books which preceded it, *A Carrack Sailed Away,* and *Street Of The Half-Moon.*

Also, Captain Angelico Chavez, O.F.M., 16th Armored Division of the Services of Our Country, Our Lady's Troubador, who remembered my work each evening in his Mass, celebrated in the South Pacific Area; and J. Manuel Espinosa, Ph.D., Division of Education and Art, State Department, Washington, D. C., an authority on Spain, for his counsel in my study of things Hispanic.

Preface

The Sixteenth Century into which the Wool Merchant of Segovia was born was a banner century for merchants. Immense and glittering fortunes were being made in the East Indies and the new Western world which exploration and long range sea transport were opening up. There was adventure there too and the glamor of strange places not only for the soldier and explorer but also for the more prosaic man of business. From the ports of Spain and Portugal and the Northern countries merchants, both young and old, were setting out on expeditions which would eventually lead them as a class not only to fabulous wealth but to a position of political honor and importance in Europe which would remain unchallenged until our own times.

The merchant, Alphonsus Rodriquez, was not unaware of these commercial opportunities, but he rejected them in favor of still larger opportunities which the age of exploration had opened up. His was the finer vision of those Catholic missionaries and explorers who brought the Faith to the Americas and to large areas in the Far East. Yet, as much as he desired to, he never himself sailed for the new lands. His part, nevertheless, in the Golden Age in the missions was an important one. It was that of opening up these new horizons for Christ to his brother Jesuits. He did this unceasingly and effectively. They, under his inspiration, went out to the new lands where he had longed to go and made a lasting contribution to the Americas and to the Far East.

We feel that Miss Farnum's modern interpretation of St. Alphonsus is particularly timely. Our postwar world in the opportunities it will offer both for commercial aggrandizement and for the salvation of souls promises to be not unlike that of the 16th Century into which the Wool Merchant of Segovia was born. We badly need his inspiration and vision.

New York, May 23, 1945

CALVERT ALEXANDER, S.J.

I

THE house of the wool merchant, Diego Rodriguez, stood in the Plaza del Azoquejo, Little Market Place, in Segovia.

A three-storied structure, with flower-filled loggias at front and sides, its yellow walls had caught the rays of the southern sun and imprisoned them. Sheltered by tall chestnut and palm trees, it peered into the Square, where all day long the Segovianos passed to and from the cloth factories and shops, and little gray asses bore wine, garden produce, and corn to the market stalls.

From the dusty plains of Castile the traveler entered Segovia through a breach in the walls opening on the Little Market Place. Above the square towered the great aqueduct which conducted the waters of the Riofrio down from the Sierra Fuenfruar, a distance of ten miles, into the old city. This mammoth bridge, nearly nine hundred feet long, was built of rough-hewn granite blocks from the Guadaramma Mountains, to northward. The country people called it El Puente del Diavolo, the Devil's Bridge, from a legend which attributed its construction to the evil one, who was supposed to have built it to please a Segovian maiden. Actually, El Puente was begun by the Roman Emperor Augustus, and continued and completed by the Emperor Trajan. This fact was indicated by holes in the granite, left by the bronze lettering of the ancient inscription.

Beginning with single arches, El Puente rose higher as the dip in the land grew more pronounced. Its upper tiers, uniform in length, gradually expanded into double arches, with the central three, the loftiest, a little over one hundred feet high.

In 1071 the aqueduct had been broken down in part by the Moors and thirty-five of its magnificent three hundred twenty arches destroyed. These had lain in ruins until 1438, when Isabella The Catholic had commissioned a monk to supervise their restoration. In 1520 the twin statues of Hercules, which had occupied niches on opposite sides of the bridge, had been taken down and statues of the Blessed Virgin and Saint Sebastian substituted for them.

Segovia had suffered many vicissitudes in her history. Under early Roman rule the town was a highly flourishing and important colony. When its inhabitants became Christians, its bishops had taken part in the councils held at Toledo in the sixth and seventh centuries. Later taken by the Mohammedans, the city had offered shelter to the faithful in the mountains. There they had practiced their religion in secret. When it was repeopled by Gallegos, from northwest Spain, it received its first charter from Alonso V, in 1108.

In the twelfth century the cathedral had been wrecked by Comuneros. A new edifice, begun in 1522, was in process of reconstruction at this time, 1541, when the Rodriguez family resided in the Plaza del Azoquejo.

In 1295 Segovia had refused to submit to the young King Ferdinand, only yielding to the heroic overtures of his mother, who pleaded his cause in the face of grave peril to her life. In 1320 the reign of Alonzo XI was attended by bloodshed in the streets of Segovia. Only a short time before Diego Rodriguez had come to the Little Market Place, many had died in the insurrection of the Comuneros. The indomitable courage and prowess of Charles V had brought peace once more to the city, and Segovia was recovering from her many wounds in an era of calm and progress.

The wool for which Segovia was famous was obtained from the flocks pastured on the Guadaramma ranges. They were driven down to the Eresma, a gentle stream, flowing beyond the city, in a green valley. Its water, while unfit for drinking, contained a property valuable for the cleansing of the wool. At the seasons of sheep shearing and the washing of the fleeces crowds of people gathered along the banks to watch the process. Later, the wool was woven into cloth on hand looms in the factories, and dispensed among the cloth shops of Segovia.

In this prosperous era, Diego Rodriguez and his wife, Maria Gomez de Alvarado, were bringing up their family of eight healthy happy boys and girls. As time went on, three other little ones were to come to bless and brighten the yellow-walled house in the Plaza del Azoquejo.

Now, in 1541, the eldest child, named Diego in honor of his father, was nearly twelve years old, and his next younger brother, Alonso, was ten. The two boys, inseparable companions, were very helpful to their parents, as they trudged about on errands to various parts of the old city, or helped about the house and in their father's wool shop.

When they were free from school and home duties, Diego and Alonso liked to wander through the maze of narrow streets whose pale old houses seemed to lean on one another, their softly tinted walls washed in pink or yellow or green or mauve. Their favorite pastime was to ascend the flight of steps at one end of the Plaza and walk on top of the city walls. These walls were so narrow in parts that Maria de Alvarado had warned them not to venture on the "allure," where the width was such that only one person at a time could pass.

High up amidst the aged bastions and the eighty-three picturesque towers, some round, some square, some octagonal, some having brick archings and ornamental designs in brick and plaster, the boys could look far off over the city and the adjacent countryside.

Sometimes Diego and Alonso went hand in hand into the Plaza Mayor, a great square hedged in by houses having many little balconies jutting out, here and there, and wooden loggias in their upper stories. At one corner, the Plaza opened, revealing the apse of the Gothic cathedral.

From the castle-fortress of the Alcazar, the former residence of the sovereigns of Leon and Castile, they could look across the wooded valley of the Eresma, to the spot where it joined waters with the Clamores, another limpid mountain stream. If they wished, they could descend into the cool valley, passing through the oldest gate in Segovia, the Puerta de Santiago, Gate of St. James, Patron of Spain.

A visit to the little "round" church of Vera Cruz, consecrated in 1208 as the Templars' Church, afforded special interest. Vera Cruz stood by the wayside, like a noble pilgrim, clad in rose and gold, close to the Geronomite Monastery, El Parral, which drowsed amidst heavy vines. Still another Christian monument of Segovia was the Church of San Estéban, St. Stephen, with a beautiful thirteenth century tower. From its gates, in the distance, the cathedral rose up, its pinnacles like the gray sails of ships in the azure sea of the sky.

Only one other church remained close by to be visited by Diego and Alonso Rodriguez on their little pilgrimages about the city. This was San Millán, situated in the valley, south of Segovia proper, close to the aqueduct. It was the finest of all the churches of the city, with its golden walls covered with vines and flowers. The boys sometimes strolled through the outer cloisters and listened to the sound of the great organ, swelling on the tropical breeze.

From almost any vantage point, the Castilian plain traveled away to the amethystine mountains, whose heads towered aloft as if reflecting the pride and austerity that characterized the people of Castile.

Diego Rodriguez, the wool merchant, had often told stories of the past glories of Spain to his two older boys, when evening had closed in, and he had returned from his work in the wool shop. A stalwart Catholic, his interest centered more in the hallowed traditions of the faith than in the rewards accruing from his business.

The young Diego was a good student and loved books, and

the stories pleased him very much. But it was Alonso, slower to learn, yet gifted with a deep insight for a child, whom his father watched with special interest as he spoke. The younger son, his oval face slight, and his expression serious, seemed rapt in the thoughts suggested by these tales of valor and high holiness.

There were many traditions of the Faith in Segovia. The thunderbolt had played a conspicuous role in certain events centering about the Church. One of these events was connected with the fortress-castle of the Alcazar, the other with the Church of Corpus Christi, which stood in the Calle de Juan Bravo, Street of Juan the Brave, named for the leader of the Comuneros.

Alfonso the Wise had expressed the then heretical opinion that the earth revolved about the sun. Hardly had he spoken the words than a thunderbolt struck the Alcazar, where he resided. He immediately recanted, and, in penitence for his "heresy," assumed the Cord of St. Francis. On the upper floor of the fortress, opposite to the throne room, was a chamber called "The Piece Of The Cord." It was decorated with the emblem of the Cord of St. Francis, in commemoration of the incident.

West of the suburb of San Lorenzo, where the Rodriguez family made their home, was the ancient Church of Corpus Christi. Formerly the property of a group of unbelievers, it had fallen into Christian hands in 1410 and was consecrated under its new name.

According to the tradition, while the faithless group were gathered inside its walls, profaning a Sacred Host which had come into their possession, the building was struck by a thunderbolt. Stricken with terror, they confessed their sacrilegious act and suffered the loss of their property as a punishment. The mark made by the thunderbolt had remained on the walls of the building, an object of reverential curiosity to the people of the city.

Sometimes, when young Diego was busy at his books, Alonso

Rodriguez would steal away by himself. Climbing the top of the city wall, he would examine with never-failing interest the two Roman tombstones, built into one part. He would walk on the top, gazing in fascination at the vista unfolded before his wondering eyes. The voices of the busy day had faded into a deep hush, broken only now and then by the clop, clop, of horses' feet, as gaily clad caballeros rode across the Plaza.

From that distance, Alonso could not hear the Eresma, singing among the reeds and rushes, but in his heart he knew the music. Sometimes the cheep, cheep, of a sleepy bird, stirring in its nest among the tall valley grasses, came to his ears, the most alive thing in all the earth in the twilight hour.

Alonso Rodriguez found what he best understood in the vast world about him, rather than in the pages of books. It was pleasant to be alone on the ancient walls when night was closing in, and silence filled his young heart like a great sound.

As Alonso looked across the Plaza, one autumn evening, from his accustomed post on the walls, he saw two unfamiliar figures crossing the aged paving stones. They were coming in the direction of the yellow house, walled in by the chestnuts and palms.

Two men. They wore the robes of ecclesiastics, with wide, soft-brimmed hats. The black cassock of one of the men was fastened at the waist by a wide flowing band. It was this man who attracted Alonso, particularly.

This priest was of medium stature. He walked with head uplifted, with a singular ease and grace, as if he trod on air. When he had drawn closer, the young boy on the wall saw that his face was very bright and kindly.

Climbing quickly down the steps, Alonso Rodriguez ran off by a back lane, to tell his parents about the strange priests, who seemed to be coming to their house in the Little Market Place.

§

Diego Rodriguez welcomed the two priests who stopped at

his door with a warmth of cordiality and a reverence that bespoke his virile Catholic faith. He ushered them into the principal room in the house, and bade them be seated, while he went to the servants' quarters to order refreshments. When he returned, the spokesman for the guests revealed their identity.

He was Father Peter Faber, priest of the young religious organization known as the Company of Jesus. His companion was Doctor Ortiz.

Father Faber stated that he had come to Segovia to preach and teach catechism in the streets, and he asked the hospitality of the Rodriguez home during the sojourn in the old walled city.

Diego Rodriguez was happy to assure Father Faber and his friend that they were most welcome to remain under his roof as long as they desired. He was deeply honored by their presence, he told them, and he was especially interested in the Company of Jesus, of which he had heard much. Until this evening, however, he had never met one of its members.

While Maria de Alvarado was tucking the younger children into the high beds, beneath the homespun blankets, after hearing their night prayers and singing them to sleep with a lullaby of Old Castile, her husband and the two oldest boys, Diego and Alonso, remained downstairs with the priests.

Diego Senior questioned Father Faber about the new Company, and listened with rapt attention to the exposition that came from the lips of the courteous and mild-mannered Jesuit, the first priest to be ordained in the organization. His simplicity, the purity of his countenance and presence, and the easy flow of his words, as he told of the beginnings of the Jesuits, enthralled Rodriguez. The two young boys seemed likewise charmed by Father Peter Faber, and listened in breathless interest to his story, much of which they could not understand.

Father Faber stated that the Founder of the Company of Jesus, Father General Ignatius of Loyola, belonged to a noble family. Born in the castle of Loyola, near the town of Azpeytia, in the province of Guipuscoa, he had grown up in gracious surroundings and had served at Court until the age of twenty-six. He had then taken up the active profession of arms.

At Pamplona, while defending that citadel against the French, he had received a wound from a cannon ball, which passed between his legs, breaking the bone of the right leg and severely wounding the flesh of the left. In admiration of his valor, his enemies had ordered him to be conveyed to his own home and there given in charge of his family and friends.

This was done. An operation on the right leg was performed, but unskillfully. This necessitated a second operation, in which the knitted bone was broken, in order that it might be stretched and adjusted properly. Although the victim of this crude surgery endured agonies of pain during the process, he uttered no cry. Only by the rigor of his facial muscles and the clenching of his hands could the surgeons know of the torments they were inflicting.

Ignatius of Loyola had begun to mend after this, although his right leg remained slightly shorter than the left. As he lay on his bed, with no possibility of active duty for the time being, he asked for a book, in order to pass the time in reading.

No book was available except an ancient Life of Christ and another on the Lives of the Saints, both printed in the Old Castilian language.

The wounded hero read both, out of sheer necessity. By degrees, the heroic sanctity depicted in the pages touched his spirit and eventually won him to the resolution of dedicating his life to the service of God.

As soon as he was able to travel, Ignatius made a pilgrimage to the famed shrine of Montserrat, after changing his fine costume for the apparel of a beggar. He laid his sword on the altar in the Virgin's Chapel of Montserrat, and made his irrevocable offering to Jesus and Mary.

As he finally turned to travel down the steep hill leading from the shrine, he saw the world stretched out before him. Plains and mountains, woods and rivers were enveloped in a gray fog, that drifted above the snow-capped Pyrenees, set far off against the horizon. Only the lone cry of an eagle disturbed the immense solitude. Then Ignatius of Loyola knew that he must win the world to Christ; that his must be the voice, crying out into the fog of a sinful humanity the story of God's love and His sublime purpose in man's creation.

Near Montserrat was the little town of Manresa, and, in a secluded spot within it, was a lonely cave in the recesses of a great rock. Ignatius of Loyola retired to this cave, which he frequented for two months, dividing his occupation between prayer and the composition of a book which he called the *Spiritual Exercises*. The rest of his time was spent in visiting the hospitals.

Leading the soul by meditation and contemplation through the Purgative, Illuminative and Unitive ways, the *Exercises* left it in the complete possession of its God, freed from the trammels of inordinate attachment to anything created.

Later, Ignatius visited the Holy Land, as a pilgrim. Here he was coldly received, for no one believed in him, and treated him like a fool . . .

And now Father Peter Faber arrived at a very intimate part of his narrative. His face shone with an inner light, and his voice dropped almost to a whisper, as he continued:

"Twelve years ago this month, in 1529, I arrived at the University of Paris. I took my bachelor's degree there, and a few months later, that of licentiate.

"My teacher was the famed Juan Pegna. However, the one who taught me the most was a young nobleman from Navarre, Master Francis Xavier. I found him to be very lovable, as well as a brilliant scholar, and I became deeply devoted to him.

"That year, Ignatius of Loyola arrived at the College of St. Barbara, where we were studying. He shared the room with Master Xavier and myself. He had come to begin the study of philosophy, and I was asked to help him, since he was much over-age for this course.

"I soon discerned that Ignatius was a most extraordinary man. We three lived, ate and worked together, sharing all things in common.

"Little by little, Ignatius won me to his way of thought, which was to fight as a militant soldier of Christ, and win souls to Him. Xavier, too, was attracted, as the plea, repeated over and over in his ear by Ignatius sounded in his ears: 'What does it profit a man if he gain the whole world and suffer the loss of his own soul?' So Xavier joined us, shortly."

Father Peter Faber did not reveal certain very personal souvenirs of his early meeting with the Soldier of Pamplona. He did not speak of the fierce struggle he had fought against violent temptations and scruples, whose nature, because of the delicate purity of his soul, was most painful to him. In desperation, he had confided in Ignatius, and the latter had calmed him, instructed him on how to overcome these troubles, and completely cured him of them.

However, Diego Rodriguez, watching the noble face of the Jesuit, knew that he cherished very intimate and wonderful memories of his first alliance with Ignatius of Loyola.

"On the Feast of Our Lady's glorious Assumption," Faber went on, "that is, seven years ago this time, on August 15, 1534, a little group of us journeyed to the shrine of Montmartre at Paris. We were seven: Masters Ignatius Loyola, Zavier, Bobadilla, Laynez, Salmeron, Simon Rodriguez, and myself.

"Diego Laynez and Alonso Salmeron had become friends while studying at Alcala; both had heard of Ignatius, and they decided to go to Paris to meet him. They did so, and joined us. At that time, Ignatius was in communication with a young Portuguese, Simon Rodriguez de Azevedo, whom the king of Portugal had sent to Paris to study. He also came in. After him came Nicolas Alfonso, called Bobadilla, from his native place. He had come to Paris from Valladolid and Alcalá, where he had been studying languages. When he heard about Ignatius and his followers, he asked to join us, and was joyfully accepted.

"It was daybreak when we climbed the hill leading to the shrine of Montmartre. We were silent, all engaged in prayer. At this time I was the only priest in the band. I had been ordained only a month before. Therefore, I celebrated Mass at the shrine. At the time of Communion, I received the vows of each member of our little company, singly, and communicated each in turn. I then pronounced my own vows, and communicated.

"Soon we had three new members, Claude le Jay, a Savoyard like myself; Paschase Brouet, of Bretancourt, near Amiens; and Jean Codure, a Provencal of Seyne, Lower Alps.

"Master Ignatius was not well at this time, and his doctor had ordered him home to his native place for the air. He went, but he stayed at a hospital and lived on alms, caring for the sick, and carrying on his apostolate. When his health was restored, he left there forever, and started to tour the cities of Spain. Soon he embarked for Genoa, and from Genoa went to Bologna. Everywhere he spoke to great crowds about the love and service of God, and brought many back to Him.

"Our little company came together at Venice in January, 1537. Master Ignatius was unable to secure passage for us to Jerusalem, as he had hoped to do. So we remained at Venice, tending the sick in the hospitals, although meeting with much opposition from the authorities, who libeled us and made our lot otherwise disagreeable. However, the furor against us soon died away.

"We decided that it would be well to present ourselves to the Pope, to acquaint him with our purpose and win his authorization for our little Company. So, in mid-Lent, we went to Rome."

Father Faber did not make known that his companion, Doctor Ortiz, had formerly been one of two very powerful opponents of the Jesuits in the Eternal City. But Ortiz had been quickly won over, and it was he who had presented the little band to the Holy Father, Pope Paul III.

"Pope Paul ordered us to hold a disputation in his presence," continued Father Faber. "We were happy over the opportunity. The disputation was held, and at its conclusion the Pope expressed himself as well satisfied with the results. He gave us his blessing, and alms, and the permission to continue our proposed journey to the Holy Land.

"At Venice, on June 24, 1537, Master Ignatius Loyola, and Masters Xavier, Laynez, Salmeron, Rodriguez, Bobadilla and Codure, were ordained priests. All said their first Masses promptly, with the exception of Father Ignatius, who waited one year, out of reverence, before offering it.

"The Holy Land pilgrimage had to be postponed because of trouble between the authorities of Venice and the Turks. So it was decided that we should separate, going different ways to conduct our apostolate of preaching and caring for the sick.

"When we asked Father Ignatius what we should reply when we were asked who we were, he answered: 'You will reply that you belong to the Company of Jesus.'

"With Father Ignatius and Father Laynez, I took the road to Rome, while our other members scattered into different cities of Italy.

"As we approached the Eternal City, about six miles out from it, Father Ignatius Loyola was granted a vision, in which he saw the Eternal Father, with Jesus, His Son, who was bearing His cross. The Eternal Father regarded Father Ignatius lovingly, and said to him: 'I will be propitious to you in Rome.' Later, our holy Founder told us about this vision, but we, of course, did not see it or hear the voice.

"We again presented ourselves before the Pope, who received us most cordially. It was arranged that Father Ignatius should give the Spiritual Exercises to persons of rank in Rome, and that Father Laynez should lecture on theology in the Collegio della Sapienza, also in the Eternal City. To me was entrusted the task of explaining the Sacred Scriptures in the same College.

"At this time, Father Ignatius Loyola learned, through a revelation, that one of ours had died at Padua, exhausted by his valiant labors for souls. He was Diego de Hoces, who became our first heavenly intercessor from the Society.

"We began to win many vocations, with the result that Father Ignatius asked the Pope to give us formal recognition as a religious society. So we were all summoned to Rome. Trouble was stirred up by enemies, but Father Ignatius appealed to the Pope to free us from the calumnies spoken against us. The Holy Father did so, and our Founder was freed and declared innocent of the trumped-up charges.

"At our first general election, we unanimously chose Father Ignatius Loyola as first General of our Company of Jesus, a life office. We then made our final vows in the Church of St. Paul in Rome. This time our beloved Founder received them, since he was now a priest.

"At the present time, our holy Founder is in Rome, at our generalate, where he is working diligently on the Constitutions and Rules of the Society. Although the Pontifical Bull of 1540, issued a year ago, limited our membership to sixty, we have now permission to receive as many as come to us.

"Recently, Father Ignatius decided to add to the group lay brothers, who will also have vows and enjoy all the privileges of the others with the exception of the ministry of the priests. It is also the thought of our Founder to establish colleges everywhere for the training of youth. At present, the other religious Orders train only those who have entered or will enter their various groups."

Diego Rodriguez was delighted to hear this concise but comprehensive account of the origin of the Jesuits, and to meet one who was a member of the Company of Jesus. On his part, Father Peter Faber was pleased that he had aroused the interest of this exemplary Catholic man, a merchant of note in the community, in the great work of the Company.

The two small sons of the Rodriguez household, Diego and Alonso, had now a new and thrilling occupation in their free time. It was to follow, at a respectful distance, the holy man, Father Peter Faber, into the streets and squares of Segovia, and watch him, as he spoke to crowds of the things of God.

At the conclusion of this outdoor mission, Father Faber was very weary. Many had returned to the Sacraments and to a better life as a result of his apostolate. Diego Rodriguez believed he should enjoy a little relaxation and quiet, with his friend and companion.

Father Peter Faber was offered the hospitality of a retreat in a country place near by, where Diego Rodriguez had an estate. Alonso, the ten-year-old son of the family, was to accompany the two men, to wait on them during their stay.

Father Faber, Doctor Ortiz and Alonso went to the country seat of the Rodriguez family. There Father Faber entered into a period of retreat, preparing by prayer and study for his future mission.

In the solitude of the woods and fields, close to the meeting-place of the two rivers, the Eresma and the Clamores, little Alonso was very happy fulfilling his important task. In return for his services, he was privileged to be taught his catechism by Father Faber, and to learn how to recite the Rosary, meditating meanwhile, on its Mysteries. Father Faber also taught Alonso to serve Mass, and so provided him with his most thrilling occupation in life so far.

The time of peaceful retreat came to a close, and, with deep regret, the Rodriguez family saw Father Faber and his friend depart from Segovia.

Alonso accompanied them across the Plaza and beneath the great arches of El Puente, the aqueduct. There he received the blessing of the Jesuit priest, who bade him remember all he had told him, and pray for the Company of Jesus.

As the boy bade farewell to his beloved friends, a great loneliness welled up in his heart.

II

FIVE years passed quietly for the Rodriguez family.

Maria, the oldest child, had married a good young man, Francis Gallego, and had gone to make her own home in another part of the city. Diego Rodriguez, Senior, went about his wool business, and in the vacation periods, Diego Junior and Alonso helped him in the shop in the Plaza del Azoquejo.

Two other little boys had since come to swell the family circle. They were named Melchior and Gaspar, for two of the Wise Kings who had followed the Star of Bethlehem to the manger of the Infant God.

Diego Rodriguez thought much about the future of his older sons. One day he spoke to his wife about the matter.

"I have heard that the Jesuits have opened a college at Alcalá, Maria," he said to her. "I think it would be well if we should send Diego and Alonso to them."

Nothing could have given more joy to the heart of Maria de Alvarado than to hear this statement from her husband's lips. She had never forgotten the saintly Father Peter Faber, whose presence in her home had brought a breath of very heaven with it.

The two boys were delighted to learn of the plan for their further education. They were soon made ready, and when the preparations for their reception at Alcalá were completed, they said "Adios" to their parents and their little brothers and sisters, and joyfully set off to share in a new and wonderful experience.

As Diego and Alonso crossed the Market Place, turning to wave a last farewell to their saintly mother, Alonso, in particular, fixed in his heart the picture of her as he would always remember and cherish it.

Maria de Alvarado was parting with her first-born sons, and her mother's heart ached a little, even though she gladly sacrificed their company for an important cause.

She stood on the wooden loggia, over the front entrance to the house, the bright colors of her wide skirt and bodice blending with those of the flowers that lifted their scented faces in the morning sunlight. Her head was covered with the little white square of muslin, tied beneath the chin, worn by all Segovian women. Her face was stained with tears, but her heart was steeled to the sacrifice she had made. Her gaze lingered longest on her little Alonso, who had cherished a deep love for Christ's Holy Mother, even as a very young child. She remembered how she had been unable to take her picture from him, and how he had cried when he had given it up.

Seen from a distance, Alcalá The Ancient seemed very imposing to the two little Segovianos, Diego and Alonso Rodriguez.

Like Segovia, it was surrounded by high walls. The houses had conical roofs, with numerous little towers jutting out from them, like the houses in other Spanish cities.

Alcalá, seated on the banks of the Henares River, had also an inspiring and picturesque history.

Moved deeply by the vision of a great Cross which appeared to him in the air, the archbishop of Alcalá had told of the apparition to Alfonso VI, who had taken over the city. The monarch gave the prelate all the lands in the vicinity of the spot where he had seen the Cross. From that time, the Toledan primates had promoted Alcalá's interests, and it had shortly become a flourishing city.

On one of the hills, the archbishop had erected a hermitage which he called Vera Cruz. However, his memory yielded place to that of another illustrious churchman, whose interest had resulted in great expansion for Alcalá. This was Cardinal Ximenez de Cisneros, a Franciscan.

This great man had received his early education in Alcalá. When he rose to prestige and power, he remembered the humble school of his youth, and raised it, in 1510, to the status of a university. He endowed it munificently, so that in time it comprised nineteen colleges and thirty-eight churches, all having independent endowments. Having been badly treated by King Ferdinand, the Cardinal had eventually returned to Alcalá, where he continued to assist the university so dear to him. So conspicuous were his achievements for it that when Francis I visited Alcalá and met the eleven thousand students of the university, he exclaimed:

"One Spanish friar has done what it would have taken a long line of kings of France to accomplish!"

Cardinal Ximenez had propagated the famous Polyglot Bible, which was printed at Alcalá, in six volumes, from 1514 to 1517. He spared nothing toward its publication, and before his death was gratified to see its final pages in type. Three copies of the Bible were printed on vellum; one for the Holy Father; one for the University of Alcalá; and one which eventually came into the possession of Louis Philippe. The text was presented in Hebrew, Latin, and Chaldaic.

The University proper was a stone structure, with cement facings. When King Ferdinand had objected to the cement as humble material, the Cardinal had replied: "It becomes me, a creature of dust, to leave marble to my successors."

Diego and Alonso Rodriguez examined, with boyish curiosity, the principal building, a three-storied structure of colored marble. In memory of its Franciscan founder, Cardinal Ximenez, it was decorated with the emblem of St. Francis' Cord. Its magnificent chapel, the grandest the boys had ever seen, was done in Gothic and Moorish style. Above the tomb of Cardinal Ximenez was his effigy, representing him, clothed in full pontifical robes, reposing on a magnificent raised urn. An epitaph recorded the illustrious achievements of the man who, at one time viceroy, then Cardinal, had ever remained a humble spiritual son of the gentle Saint of Assisi.

Diego and Alonso Rodriguez were given in charge to a Jesuit scholastic, Brother Peter Villaneuve, a young religious, brilliantly endowed with learning. In his earlier life he had been very poor, working as a servant. Father Ignatius Loyola had met him in Rome, and had conceived such a high opinion of his virtue and talents that he had entrusted him to Father Simon Rodriguez, one of the Founder's first companions in the Company. Father Rodriguez had sent Peter from Coimbra to Alcalá, to continue his studies at the latter university.

Brother Villaneuve was a very homely young man, swarthy in complexion and awkward in his movements. He had reached Alcalá in 1543, and had received lodging, out of charity, in the room of a venerable professor. Soon it was evident that his spirituality was of such a high order that the most famous professors in the place came to consult him and ask his prayers. Over the students he exercised an extraordinary influence, and numbers had entered religious life through that influence and his holy example.

Father Ignatius Loyola entertained great hopes of this young Jesuit. Father Peter Faber had also encouraged him. When Father Faber had preached before the Infantas of Spain, he had won their promise to assist in the support of a Jesuit College, to be established as a part of the university. A house had been found for the foundation, and Father Faber had promised to send to it two scholastics and a lay brother from Coimbra.

Brother Villaneuve was the Jesuit commissioned to find the house. He found one, but it was so wretched that its owner told him he might have it, if he would clean it and put it in order.

Brother Villaneuve lost no time in preparing the poor place for its great role. He cleaned and renovated it with his own hands, so that it was somewhat fit to serve as a residence and college.

In this house the Jesuits were living when Diego and Alonso Rodriguez came to Alcalá. The two boys found that the lodgings assigned to them were far from comfortable, as their own home had been. It seemed as if every material advantage was lacking to it. However, the sublime courage and abnegation of Brother Peter Villaneuve evoked a response from all the boys under his charge, and all made the best of their surroundings.

For recreation, Brother Villaneuve sometimes led the boys about the university city, and pointed out to them the monuments of historical interest and other souvenirs of departed days. Sometimes these walks led along the banks of the Henares, which, because of its rocky bed, was called River of Stones. From a section known as San Antonio, outside the city walls, the town could be seen to excellent advantage, rising in a ragged outline of crumbling battlements, with the beautiful gardens of the Mendoza Palace hanging over a wild ravine.

The principal church of Alcalá, El Magistral, rose at the Western city limits. It was a Gothic edifice, originally dedicated to SS. Justo and Pastor, aged seven and nine years respectively. They had been put to death for the faith in 306, and their remains were preserved in the church. Diego and Alonso wondered about these young saints, and were glad that they could pray at their shrine.

With the other boys, they enjoyed the delicious honey for which a suburb of Alcalá, Guadalajara, was famed. Its fine flavor was absorbed from the many aromatic herbs which clothed the hillsides in the vicinity.

A year passed in this pleasant place, with Diego and Alonso Rodriguez advancing in their studies under the skilled tutelage of Brother Villaneuve. Diego learned quickly and was a very ambitious student. Alonso was slow, but a faithful boy. Noting his rare piety and modesty, Brother Villaneuve was careful to foster these virtues in every way possible.

This noble-souled young Jesuit was deeply pained when one day he received word of the death of Diego Rodriguez, Senior. The two boys were instructed to return home at once.

The wool merchant of Segovia had been many days laid at rest when his older sons reached their home in the Plaza del Azoquejo. Once again Diego and Alonso crossed the square, and came to the house with the yellow walls. This time a shadow lay across it, not cast by the giant aqueduct. It was the shadow of a new and poignant sorrow, and it was hard to bear.

Maria de Alvarado received her boys with wide opened arms, and folded them to her heart. She told them of the sacred souvenirs of their father's passing from earth. Then she scrutinized them carefully. She observed that Diego had grown more manly and confident, but that Alonso looked very pale, and a little thinner than she cared to see.

After awhile, future plans were discussed. Diego Rodriguez Senior had been a man of fervent Christian life and ideals. He had maintained his pleasant home and his large family – there were eleven at the time of his death – in comfort and peace. An unworldly man, he had not prospered above the average in his business. Now there was not much left to divide among so large a family.

Diego was already studying for his degree and gave such promise that Maria de Alvarado decided to permit him to return to the university at Alcalá. Alonso was selected to remain at home and learn his father's business.

Diego was greatly pleased over his opportunity. Alonso was quite content to remain in Segovia and assist his mother. His only regret was that he must part with his beloved teacher, Brother Peter Villaneuve.

Diego returned to Alcalá and Alonso remained behind. The days passed, then the months. Those in the yellow house in the Market Place began to feel, somewhat, the pinch of want. Having no daughter at home old enough to help her in the management and work of a good-sized house, Maria Gomez de Alvarado was obliged to work very hard, and to dismiss the servants. Alonso kept the shop, with her advice and encouragement.

Maria de Alvarado often spoke to her boys about the holy man, Father Peter Faber, who had come as a guest to her home one evening in August, a few years before. She did not know that Father Faber was now in Rome, whither he had gone to join his Founder, Father General Ignatius Loyola. She had heard that Father General Ignatius had instituted the custom of having provincialates for the various places where the Company functioned. He had appointed Father Aroaz, a very able man, as first Provincial of Aragon, the Province in which Segovia was situated.

Important events in addition to this had occurred in the Company in recent years. Father Ignatius had commissioned Father Peter Faber, during the latter's visit to Gandia, in Spain, to work there for the promotion of the Company's interests. Faber had gone to Gandia, and had met its Duke, Francis Borgia, a remarkable man. The wife of this nobleman had recently died, and the Duke had wished to consult Father Faber on a matter of the utmost moment.

Some time before his wife's decease, the Duke had looked into the open coffin in which the body of the Empress Isabella reposed. She had been dead some days, and her countenance was so disfigured that Francis Borgia had conceived a very strong impression of the transitoriness of this life and the importance of eternity. He was a man of great fervor, and he had already vowed to enter a religious order when his wife departed from this life. He wished to talk with Father Faber, in order to determine which order he should choose.

Under Father Faber's direction, the Duke went through the Spiritual Exercises. When he had finished, he had resolved to become a Jesuit.

While Father Faber remained in the ducal palace, a remarkable incident had occurred. He was kneeling, one day, with others, in the family chapel. As he was looking upon a lovely painting of the Blessed Virgin, near the altar, the eyes of the painting suddenly opened very wide, and fixed themselves lovingly upon him. The incident was seen by all, and all realized that Father Faber must be very close to heaven.

Faber had left Spain and gone back to Rome. The Duke of Gandia had entered the Company, of which he was destined to become the third General, and was recognized as a man of great discernment, talent, and holiness of soul. Other events of great importance were happening to the little group of Father Ignatius Loyola's sons. However, Maria de Alvarado did not know about them.

In a corner of the best room in the house, Maria kept the armchair in which Father Faber had sat on the evening when he had come to her home. No one ever occupied it, now. No one ever would. As if by instinct, the children seemed to know that it was reserved by their holy mother, and that other chairs must serve them.

Young Alonso Rodriguez went about his daily duties in the wool shop quietly, but without great efficiency. His mother supervised the business. She made no complaint that it did not flourish, and she was happy when she observed that Alonso spent many of his spare hours in the parish church of St. Coloma, praying, and attending the services. He was a generous, obedient, kind, and innocent boy, but he did not seem to be gifted with the brilliance which distinguished the oldest son of the family.

Maria de Alvarado often wondered what was in store for this boy, who was so dear to her. . . .

In his heart, Alonso knew that he was not to spend his life in a shop, selling woolen cloth. He was to spend it somewhere else. He did not know where.

He was certain of it. If his own heart had not told him so, the eyes of Brother Peter Villaneuve, as they had regarded him with a singular understanding and affection, promised it.

III

DIEGO Rodriguez finished his course at the University of Alcalá and entered the University of Salamanca, where he took up the study of law. Maria de Alvarado, Alonso and the other members of the family were very proud of his success and ready to make every sacrifice so that he might go on to the end, and receive his degree. His teacher at Salamanca was the famous Doctor Covarruvias, the friend and helper of St. Teresa of Ávila.

Diego remained faithful to his home and family obligations, and wrote frequent letters to his beloved mother. The teachings of saintly Brother Peter Villanueve had borne good fruit in his heart and mind.

Time passed, and Diego married a worthy young woman and started his own home, carrying on his profession of law. However, matters did not go as well with Maria de Alvarado and Alonso.

One after another, fierce wars, under Charles V, involving all Spain, brought on serious economic troubles. In 1552 the Cortes, who formulated the laws, forbade the export of cloth from Spain, as well as spun and combed wool. Heavy taxes were imposed on the exportation of all manufactured goods and on the importation of raw materials. It was inevitable that the home manufacturing plants closed down, after trying to struggle along under such desperate circumstances. Those of the affluent class showed a decided preference for clothing made abroad, and conditions went from bad to worse in the cities of Spain.

The widow of Diego Rodriguez Senior was a practical woman. She believed that her son, Alonso, needed a helpmate and the responsibilities which a home and family of his own would bring. Also, a bride would bring a substantial dowry with her, and so turn what seemed approaching failure for Alonso into success.

Maria broached the subject to Alonzo, one evening, after he had come in from the shop in the Plaza.

"I think it would be well for you to marry, Alonso," she said, quietly. "What do you think of Maria Suarez, of Pedraza? She is a fine girl, and comes of good family."

Maria Suarez was scarcely known to Alonso. He only knew that she lived with her father in the neighboring walled town, and that she was worthy of the best any young man could give her. If he was somewhat stunned by his mother's sudden proposition, he did not betray the fact. Accustomed to obedience and respect for his parents, and with innate Spanish courtesy in his veins, Alonso acquiesced. It remained for Maria de Alvarado to visit the family of the prospective bride, and see what arrangements could be made.

This was done. Since no difficulty stood in the way of the proposed union, Maria Suarez, the daughter of a prosperous grazier of Pedraza, was joined in marriage to Alonso Rodriguez. Alonso was twenty-six years of age, Maria a few years younger.

In a convenient place, close to the old parish church of St. Eulalia in Segovia, the young couple took up residence. This was one of the most lively spots in Segovia, for it was close to a wide open field, where the cloth and wool fairs were held. The houses in the neighborhood were singularly picturesque, with slender colonnades adorning them in front, and magnificent mountains looking down upon them. The Church of St. Eulalia was also picturesque, having a number of quaint round arches set into its sturdy tower.

After his marriage, Alonso Rodriguez went regularly to the wool shop, always stopping in to visit his mother before going home at the end of the day. He noted with apprehension that she was becoming more frail, and he wished to spare her as much of her burden as possible. He had always been a kind son and brother, and now he was a kind husband. Maria Suarez, his young wife, asked only that he might long be spared to her, and that their children might be many and devoted.

Segovia had a new bishop at this time. He was a member of the Order of St. Jerome, Fray Francisco de Benavides. He was very anxious to have a college of the Jesuits in Segovia, as were Don Lewis Mendoa and Don Ferdinand de Solier, minor canon and archpriest respectively, of the Cathedral. The two latter ecclesiastics had met the Founder of the Company of Jesus, and they cherished a deep-seated respect and admiration for him.

Bishop Benavides communicated this wish to Father Francis

Borgia, formerly Duke of Gandia, now a Jesuit priest and Commissary General of the Company in Spain. The bishop besought Father Borgia to send to Segovia some of his religious, to establish there a work for the youth.

Father Borgia was happy to comply with the plea. On February 20, 1559, two years after the marriage of Alonso Rodriguez to Maria Suarez, the first Fathers and Brothers of the Company arrived in the city. One of the priests was Father Ferdinand Solier, a nephew of the canon. The little group took up their residence in a rented house, near the Church of San Martin, one of the finest churches in Segovia. The chapel of the church was given over to their use for hearing confessions and distributing Holy Communion to the people.

Father Francis Borgia chose a very saintly and learned man, Father Lewis Santander, as first rector of the new institute. Father Santander reached Segovia at the beginning of June of that year. With him were three novices, who were to enter upon their work as teachers.

All the city rejoiced over the coming of these first Jesuits who were to remain permanently in their midst.

No one was happier over this event than Maria de Alvarado and Alonso. At the earliest opportunity, Alonso made the acquaintance of Father Lewis Santander. He rejoiced to find him a most zealous and prudent, as well as erudite religious. Father Santander had been the early disciple of the venerable John of Ávila, and was already a doctor when he entered the Company of Jesus. He was a preacher of distinguished merits and an enlightened spiritual director, who had served as guide for St. Teresa when she was about to visit Segovia, to make a foundation there.

Father Santander delivered his first sermon in Segovia on the Sunday following the Octave of Corpus Christi, June 4. So profound was the impression which he made that he was at once asked to preach in other churches of the city. He did so, and wrought a great change for the better among all classes.

Living humbly in the little rented house, the Fathers of the Company inaugurated their school with a discourse delivered by one of the novices, Brother José de Acosta. They then began the work of teaching catechism, with hundreds of the children attending the classes.

Maria de Alvarado was privileged to be able to send her younger children to these classes, and she herself chose a Jesuit as her director. Her older children did likewise.

It was evident that Bishop de Benavides had done a very useful thing in introducing these religious into Segovia. For not only the boys and girls, but the adults gathered about the Jesuit Fathers in crowds, anxious to receive their instruction.

In August of this year an important happening occurred. This was the visit of Father Francis Borgia to Segovia. His coming was intended to encourage and promote the new foundation of the Company. On the feast day of St. Bartholomew he preached in the Cathedral. All the townspeople who could gain admittance were there to hear him. They knew that he was a man who had renounced a high position and a life of affluence in the world to become a member of a young, and not so well known Company.

Father Borgia's presence brought great happiness and honor to the people, and they were grateful to him for his visit.

Alonso Rodriguez, sitting beneath the pulpit in the Cathedral, listened to Father Borgia. He found in the sermon something that appealed very strongly to his sensitive ardent nature. Under the spiritual guidance of Father Lewis Santander, he was at peace, and making steady progress in the spiritual life. His cup of happiness seemed filled to overflowing.

On January 16, 1560, a little son was born to Alonso Rodriguez and Maria Suarez. He was given the name, Gaspar, in Baptism, and St. Antony of Padua was assigned as his Patron. Maria de Alvarado was one of the two godmothers selected for the child.

Two years passed by and in January, 1562, the Visitor General of the Company of Jesus came to Segovia. He was Father Nadal, and he came to select a site for a new college. His choice was a spot close to the old city walls. Father Nadal arranged that the house selected should be adapted, as far as possible, to serve as temporary college.

These arrangements were carefully followed out. A lowly chapel was fitted up in the house, and the Eucharistic Saviour took up his abode there on December sixth of that year. However, before the Divine Tenant of the tabernacle deigned to come to occupy His new home, He had sent a second little one to bless and gladden Alonso Rodriguez and his wife. He was named for his father, Alonso.

Following his wool business, day by day, Alonso's solicitude for his little family increased, as he saw his proceeds from the sale of wool gradually diminishing. He worked harder than ever, but he found it difficult to collect the moneys due him from negligent patrons, and many debts were listed on his books.

He saw with gratification the slow but steady progress made by the Jesuits in Segovia, and he went regularly to his confessor, Father Santander, to disclose to him the state of his conscience. Father Santander was a very enlightened guide, and when he observed how much Alonso desired to improve, he helped him in every way he could.

Alonso had moved with his little family to a near-by parish, St. Juste. He had now his wife, Maria, and three little ones, Gaspar, Alonso, and a little girl, also Maria.

His happiness in his beloved ones was to be short-lived, however. First Gaspar, then little Maria sickened and died. Bent, but not broken by this succession of sorrows, Alonso comforted his stricken young wife as best he could. He saw, with a dread foreboding, that her health drooped, from day to day.

The doctor began to pay regular visits to the house. But his efforts were of no avail. Maria Suarez left her husband, and his one remaining child, little Alonso, and took her place in the quiet Campo Santo, beside her two little ones.

Alonso was now a widower, with one small son. It seemed as if his whole world had crashed down about him and that he had gone down with it.

Besides his mother, his two unmarried sisters, Antonia and Juliana, remained close to him. The two young women had dedicated themselves to God and were living lives of piety in their old home. Alonso came to live with them, and Maria de Alvarado assumed the care of the little Alonso, trying to take a mother's place to both the bereaved father and child.

Alonso Rodriguez had enjoyed only four happy years of married life when sorrows had come upon him, in swift succession. Father Santander guided him securely over this hard path of desolation and loneliness; the Jesuit director believed that God had special designs on the pure-souled, stronghearted man, who found his solace in prayer and the Sacraments.

Peace gradually returned to the heart of Alonso. His mother had watched with breaking heart the transformation of her second son from a happy and contented husband and father into a recluse whose stooped shoulders and bent head revealed the burdens under which he suffered. Mary Alvarado, perhaps, wondered if she had acted wisely in suggesting matrimony to this quiet, deeply spiritual man. She had done what she believed was right. But God had not disposed that her Alonso was to enjoy for long what she had hoped and intended for him.

And then, one day, when Maria Alvarado believed that Alonso had somewhat regained his former composure, she felt very ill, and was forced to lie down on her bed. She was so ill that Alonso and his two sisters summoned the family doctor.

The doctor came. Alonso saw him, like a gray shadow, entering the door, as he had entered the little house in the parish of St. Juste.

The doctor examined the sick woman and prescribed for her. But he shook his head. There was no hope. Maria de Alvarado had finished her work in the house with the yellow walls, under the chestnut and palm trees. Her time had come.

Soon, with his little Alonso clinging fast to his hand, Alonso Rodriguez walked behind the mortal remains of his good mother, and saw her lifted into her last resting place. He dried the tears of Antonia and Juliana, and tried to comfort and encourage the other members of the family, some of whom had come from a distance to attend the solemn obsequies.

Father Santander stood by his beloved spiritual son to the last, and, when all was over, accompanied him back to the College and led him into the presence of his Sacramental Lord.

The Jesuit director said nothing to Alonso of his belief that God was working out some very special plan for his future life. He waited, watched, and prayed for Alonso.

Soon he permitted this extraordinary man to begin the then uncommon practice among the faithful of communicating each week. Out of devotion to the Blessed Virgin, Alonso chose one of her feasts, Our Lady of the Snow, on which to begin these weekly Communions. That year the Feast fell on Sunday.

Father Santander fully approved when Alonso asked him whether it might not be well for him to give up the wool business and retire to a little hermitage in his mother's house, there to live a life of prayer and penance. His little Alonso was to be left in charge of his two saintly sisters, Antonia and Juliana. Sufficient funds were available so that he could support himself, and the others, living frugally.

But there were to be only two others for Alonso to care for. His little Alonso, pining for his mother and his little playmates, followed them into eternity in a very short time. More than ever, Father Santander felt that this was the hand of the Lord, working for His own special design.

Soon after Alonso had entered upon his new way of life, as he slept one night, a vision appeared to him. He saw his Divine Lord, surrounded by twelve saints, clothed in celestial splendor. His holy Patron, St. Francis of Assisi, was among them. Stepping forward from the group, St. Francis asked him: "Why do you weep so much?"

Alonso replied: "How can I help weeping, when I know how grave my sins are, since I know that merely a venial sin committed against God deserves to be wept over for a lifetime?"

St. Francis comforted him and seemed to approve his way of life. Then Alonso awoke, but he remembered what had occurred in his sleep as if it were happening before him.

Father Santander listened to the account of this dream and was much impressed by the vision. Soon he was to be even more impressed, as Alonso described a second vision with which he had been favored.

In spirit, he had seen a dense flight of birds, black, and rising into the sky like a great tower. Then a beautiful white bird, having on it the letters of the Holy Name, I.H.S., had descended into their midst and created such havoc by its presence that most of the others took to flight. The dove swooped down upon the black birds, and pierced them to death.

The priest believed that the time was now ripe to discuss the meaning of this dream with his penitent. He told Alonso that, to his manner of thinking, it signified that he was to enter the Company of Jesus. But, he added, after he had entered, he would be called upon to endure terrible assaults of the evil one. However, with the aid of heaven, he would emerge victorious.

Alonso's heart and soul were filled with joy to hear from the lips of his saintly guide what he had hardly dared to think of— that he was called to the life of the Company he so greatly loved and admired.

Under Father Santander's direction, he entered more deeply still into the mysteries of the Life of Christ. His confessor observed that he advanced in the divine knowledge swiftly and marvelously from that time on.

As he one day observed Alonso, who was absorbed in contemplation, groping his way along by the wall of the church, Father Santander cautioned him not to allow himself to indulge in these visitations when he was outside, because others would be quick to take scandal from them.

Quite obedient, Alonso followed the advice.

His love for his Blessed Mother was such that once he said to her, aloud: "I love you more than you love me!"

He was startled to hear the answer: "No. I love you more than you love me."

In 1566 Father Santander was called from his post of rector at Segovia, to Valencia, where the Society had recently founded the College of St. Paul. A new rector, Father Juan de Leon, was appointed in his stead. Father Martínez, one of the priests stationed in the College of Segovia, now became Alonso's confessor, and Alonso found him very sympathetic and understanding.

For nearly three years Alonso continued his life of prayer and penance in the world, under Father Martínez' direction. He considered his past sins as a stumbling-block to his progress, but his confessor knew differently.

Alonso was now thirty-eight years old. His education was deficient and his strength had been greatly weakened by the trials through which he had passed. He hardly dared to think he would be of use in fulfilling the duties of a lay brother in the Company, yet he believed that God wanted him to be a Jesuit.

Father Martínez was very anxious to secure his admission to the novitiate. But when he asked the other Fathers of the College to speak for him, one and all declined to do so. They alleged that Alonso was overage, and lacking in the health necessary for the Company.

One only hope stirred in the heart of the sorely disappointed man. He remembered Father Santander, now at Valencia. He determined to make the long journey from Segovia to that city, to find his friend, and ask his advice. Whatever the decision of Father Santander should be, he was resolved to abide bv it.

Before starting for Valencia, he deeded what little property remained as his share of the family goods to his sisters, Antonia and Juliana.

It was early winter when he left Segovia forever, with the

blessing of Father Martínez, to find his life work. He did not know what the future held in store. But he knew that the faithful spiritual son of Father Ignatius Loyola, his former director, would have the answer to his problem. Somehow, it seemed to Alonso that a certain pattern was stamped on all the spiritual soldiers of the Company of Jesus. It was the pattern of perfect obedience to God's leading: *Ad Majorem Dei Gloriam*—For the Greater Glory of God.

IV

EARLY in the New Year of 1569 Alonso Rodriguez arrived in Valencia, garden city of Spain, lying a little more than two miles inland from the shores of the Mediterranean, on the right bank of the Guadalaviar, which the Arabs had christened "White River," from the crystal brightness of its waters.

He had journeyed along the coastal plain, a brilliant flowering tract in places where the soil was well irrigated, through a country vastly different from the arid land of Castile. Even in winter, it was a maze of tall waving palms, with almond, peach and apple groves, vineyards and olive plantations spreading a rich perfume over the province.

He had passed villages of low, white chimneyless cottages, having quaint pointed gables and thatched roofs. After crossing an iron bridge, a little beyond an old Hieronymite convent, San Miguel de los Reyes, he saw the silhouette of the city of Valencia against the skyline.

Valencia Province, from which the city took its name, although very small, was one of the most fertile and beautiful in all Spain. The Moors had believed that their paradise was suspended above it, and that a portion had fallen to the earth, to become the regal city. In this flowering terrain, or huerta, the Jesuits had established a College, where they received the youth who wished to pursue higher studies in an atmosphere permeated by religion.

Entering the old city wall, Alonso Rodriguez found himself in the principal street of Valencia, the Calle de San Vicénte. Near and afar, the gold and white and dark blue domes of the numerous churches were etched under a soft southern sky. The cool fingers of the west wind touched his cheeks as he hastened to inquire the way to the new College of St. Paul, the Jesuit foundation.

He was directed, with true Spanish courtesy, by a group of Valencian men. They wore the wide linen breeches, called bragas, confined at the waist by a red sash; a short velvet jacket and headcloth, the latter of gaily colored material: leggings patterned after those worn by the Greeks, and the hempen sandals, called espertenas.

There were no women in the streets. Alonso did not see that some of them looked down from the balconies of the houses, conversing with their male relatives or friends below. The Valencian women were among the most fascinating of all Spanish ladies; their complexion was lighter than that of the men. Their garments were full and richly colored, and their hair was done in high rolls, ornamented by a great silver-gilt pin, engraved with the image of the loved patroness of their city, Nuestra Señora de los Desparados, Our Lady of the Helpless.

The Jesuit College of St. Paul was located in a retired part of Valencia. Following the instructions given him, Alonso Rodriguez found the buildings, close to one section of the city wall.

He had written to Father Santander, his former confessor, of his proposed visit. He was very happy when the kindly Jesuit received him with open arms, and spent a long time listening to his account of the recent past, and discussing his vocation.

The priest questioned Alonso carefully as to his ideas and desires. Then he gave his verdict—that he believed Alonso should resume his studies, in preparation for the priesthood in the Company of Jesus. Father Santander also thought that

Alonso should take up some useful work, in order to earn his livelihood until such time as he should be admitted to the novitiate.

Alonso had nothing of material value in his possession, since he had given his portion of the family funds to his sisters, before leaving Segovia. Father Santander, however, with the assistance of some of the other Jesuits in the house, furnished him with a small sum of money, and advised him to visit the other religious foundations in Valencia, and ask alms, to tide him over the period of waiting.

This advice was followed. Humbly the former wool merchant went from door to door of the religious houses, asking help. This procedure was not unusual in that day, when alms were frequently disbursed to poor but worthy students.

When he discerned how spiritual and how faithful Alonso was, one of the theology students at the College of St. Paul gave him a comparatively large sum, much more than he had received elsewhere. Another, who proved a friend in need, was a good lay brother, the porter of the College, Brother Jerome Espinel. Brother Espinel was a man of exceptionally holy life, and he quickly recognized in another the spirituality he so greatly admired. He not only gave some money to Alonso, but furnished him with excellent advice, which was gratefully accepted.

Alonso knew that Father Ignatius Loyola had started in to study at Barcelona at the age of thirty-nine, among the boys in the lower Latin classes. He took heart from this remembrance, and turned zealously to his books. He endured patiently the sarcastic taunts and the ridicule of certain students, who were less kind and enlightened than others. He paid no attention to them, but, in the time between his studies and classes, gave himself up to prayer and penance.

One of the greatest blessings of his new life was the fact that Father Santander had again become his spiritual guide. But Father Santander realized that Alonso could not go on indefinitely, seeking alms throughout the city and at the same time apply himself, with a quiet mind, to his studies. So, he found a post for his penitent as tutor to the young son of a merchant of Valencia.

Alonso was thankful for this opening. His duties comprised going to and from school with the little fellow, and teaching him to read.

The merchant, Ferdinand Chencillos, was delighted with the results of this companionship. He sensed that Alonso was a very unusual man, and he felt that his child was fortunate to have him as tutor and friend. From Father Santander, Chencillos learned much about Alonso's life and character, and he was pleased to assist one who was so worthy and who intended to become a Jesuit.

Despite his new-found consolation, Alonso felt a great fear lest he should not be accepted by the Company. He realized that he was slow to learn from books, and that he was over-age for the novitiate. Too, he was aware that his health had been greatly impaired by his sorrows and austere manner of life.

Father Santander encouraged him, when he laid these fears open to him, and watched with an ever increasing solicitude over his progress.

From the house of the genial merchant, Alonso passed to the palace of a noble lady of Valencia. This lady was a member of an illustrious Sicilian family, and she was very desirous that her son, Lewis de Mendoza, should have Alonso's services as tutor. On Father Santander's glowing recommendation, Alonso found occupation in this charge, and was enabled to pay his living expenses very easily.

For two years he continued the study of rhetoric under famous masters of the Company of Jesus. He was not a brilliant student, but his professors recognized that he possessed virtues of a high order, and they begrudged no effort in the attempt to aid him.

Father Santander told Alonso that the time was now ripe for admission to the Company, and counseled him to ask for it.

As he was about to follow this advice, an incident occurred

which might have forestalled his action, had he not confided in his confessor.

It was vacation time, and Alonso gladly accepted the invitation of one of the students, a man of his own age, to visit him in the near-by town of San Mateo. This man had left the College rather suddenly, a short time before. He was living in a hermitage which he had arranged for himself, and he wanted to ask Alonso to join him in this way of life.

When Alonso reached the hermitage, and the two men talked together, the hermit told him that he should not return to Valencia, but should remain there and live a solitary life in the little hut.

Alonso was sorely tempted to remain, for the life appealed to him. However, although the hermit employed every means of trying to force his decision, he returned to Valencia, to tell Father Santander about his new-born desire.

When he reached the College of St. Paul, he went at once to Father Santander, and told him what he had done. Already, he felt somewhat uneasy about the whole affair, and he asked the priest what he thought about it.

Father Santander was thoroughly displeased with Alonso. However, he was not harsh in his remarks. He simply said:

"What is this, Alonso? I realized that you had not been to see me for some time? Now I am very much afraid you will lose your soul."

Alonso was greatly disturbed when he heard this. "But why should I lose it, Father?" he asked.

"Because," the Jesuit replied, "I see that you want to follow your caprice, and if you do so, there can be no doubt that you will be lost."

At once, all desire for a hermit's life left Alonso's mind. He realized that he had acted unwisely in dallying with the temptation, because he had previously made up his mind to become a Jesuit, if he should be accepted by the Company.

He knelt at Father Santander's feet and promised: "Father,

as long as I live, I will never again follow my own will. You may do with me whatever you like."

Father Santander then instructed Alonso to ask for admittance into the Company without delay. He told him to pray to the Blessed Virgin for success, then to leave matters in her blessed hands.

Alonso followed the advice. Through Father Santander, he presented his request to the counselors of the College. His confessor had asked that he might be received as a lay brother postulant, for he realized that Alonso's studies had not progressed as favorably as was necessary for the priesthood.

Father Santander was deeply grieved when the counselors were not in favor of admitting him. They alleged his advanced age, his frail state of health and the fact that he had not done well in his studies as their reason for the decision.

Very dissatisfied with this finding, Father Santander suddenly thought of one resource left to him. He decided to make use of it, and see what would happen.

Providentially, Father Cordeses, the Provincial, was visiting the College of St. Paul at that time. He had come to Valencia to attend a meeting of Jesuit Provincials of the Company. After the meeting, he had stayed on for a little while.

Father Santander went to Father Cordeses and told him about Alonso.

The Provincial, a Catalan, was a very spiritual and gifted man. He had formerly been a notary at Barcelona, and he had ripe experience of the world and of human nature. He had served as rector of the College of Gandia, founded by Father Francis Borgia. He had twice been provincial of Aragon, and in the interval between his two terms in the high office had held the rectorship at Coimbra. He was distinguished for a great devotion to the Mother of God, and his fellow Jesuits looked on him as a saint, believing that he had never forfeited his baptismal innocence. This was the man who now examined the vocation of Alonso Rodriguez.

Father Cordeses sent for Alonso and spoke with him for some time. At the conclusion of the interview he dismissed him, giving him some cause to believe his suit was favorably regarded.

When Alonso had gone from his presence, steeped in a holy joy and anticipation, Father Cordeses called the consultors together. He said to them, in words to be forever famous in the annals of the Company of Jesus:

"Well, Fathers, I have had a talk with Alonso, and examined carefully into his life and purpose. And I feel obliged to admit him as a saint, for I intend he shall be one, and a great one, and he will give great glory to the Company by his virtues and example."

Confounded and surprised, the counselors could say nothing against the verdict of one whom they considered to be inspired in all he did. So, it was arranged that Alonso Rodriguez should be admitted to his novitiate in the College of St. Paul on the following day.

When Father Cordeses told him of the decision, Alonso humbly thanked him, then sought Father Santander and poured out his joy and gratitude for the wonderful favor of which, however, he believed himself quite unworthy. Father Santander referred all the credit for the acceptance to Father Cordeses, of whom he said: "The Provincial is a man of exceptional piety and discernment. Six years ago he insisted upon receiving a young peasant lad from the mountains. This youth's name was Juan Ximenes. The counselors felt that he would be of no use to us. Father Cordeses, however, saw more deeply than they. He read the interior of the boy, and discerned there a rare holiness. He received him. When he became one of us, Juan joined to a love of hard work such a marvelous spirit of prayer and, in particular, such a love for our Lord's sacred passion that the Fathers soon came to reverence him and ask his prayers. His early death removed from the ranks of the Company one whom all deemed a saint.

"So, Father Cordeses, gifted in the knowledge of hearts, has accepted you, Alonso. You are to remain here with us and justify our expectations by learning to become a good Jesuit."

Alonso prayed long and fervently that night, thanking his Lord for the wonderful favor he had won.

As he was about to retire for the night, he heard a pounding on the shutters of his window. The room was located on the first floor, and opened on the grounds of the College.

Throwing back the shutters, he was alarmed and horrified to see there the hermit of San Mateo, his face distorted with rage. The hermit began to reproach him for having rejected his invitation to join him.

Alonso did not reply. Quickly closing the shutters, he thanked God for having delivered him from a snare which might have ruined his whole life.

The morning of January 31, 1570, found Alonso Rodriguez, a lay brother postulant of the Company of Jesus, beginning his religious life at Valencia. His period of probation had started, and he had nothing more to seek.

Because the foundation at Valencia was comparatively recent, it lacked many conveniences, including a separate establishment for the lay brothers. At this time the novices of the Company were receiving their training at Saragossa. The superiors decided not to send Alonso there, but to retain him, partly because of Father Cordeses' prophecy, partly because of the difficulties of transportation between the several provinces of the Company in Spain.

The new lay brother postulant was overjoyed to find that the first exercise of his religious life was to spend an entire month making the *Spiritual Exercises* as composed by Father Ignatius Loyola. What had been very difficult to him in the study of the secular sciences was very easy in the language of heaven. Father Santander was hardly surprised to find, that, as he advanced in the exercises, Alonso absorbed their content and spirit most thoroughly.

As he continued in this marvelous study, he was edified and consoled to recognize a master hand in the author of this remarkable book. From the foundation, which set forth man's absolute dependence on God as his first beginning and his final end, through the great mysteries of the Redemption, the purgative, the illuminative, and the unitive ways, he traveled in spirit, realizing more and more how fortunate he was in being called to the life of the Company.

He learned how wise the holy founder was in legislating for his own group of temporal coadjutors, seven years after the foundation of his great work. Many who were not adapted for the priesthood by nature or talents, could become fully privileged religious of the Company of Jesus, having the three vows of poverty, chastity, and obedience, and the fortunate work of employing themselves in useful temporal duties in the houses of their society. Undistracted by the grave burdens, cares, and responsibilities of the priestly office, they might enjoy an unbroken union with God, while performing humble menial tasks in the home or foreign missions. Some there had been who, while possessing all the training and talents requisite for priesthood in the Company—had offered themselves as lay brothers, preferring to serve God in this state because of its special opportunities of sanctifying themselves and serving souls. Generally the Company did not accept such candidates for the temporal coadjutorship, believing that all talents should be utilized according to their possibilities.

From the first, his superiors found it necessary to curtail the penances inflicted upon himself by Brother Alonso Rodriguez. He accepted their judgment without murmuring, but often he prayed to his Divine Lord:

"You know, Lord, how I hate this wicked flesh of mine, and how I wish in every way to afflict it. But I prefer still more the guidance of those whose judgment is to be my law."

His novice master gave Brother Rodriguez permission to use his well-loved corporal penances once a month, only. But soon a trial came upon him which caused him the greatest sufferings of mind and soul, a trial which no penances could assuage.

His mind and heart became filled with thoughts of fear, as he dwelled on the terrible consequences he believed would follow his past sins.

As an antidote to this trial, his confessor told him to fly instantly to God, when such thoughts came. He did so, but the trial persisted for a long time.

Occasionally Brother Rodriguez went with one of the Community, or alone, on an errand of one kind or other about the city. Although he came to know the principal streets and the characteristics of the lovely province, he never allowed himself to enjoy the natural beauties all about him. As in Segovia, his delight was, when he had a few extra moments of freedom, to visit some of the churches.

In the mild dry climate of the province, Brother Rodriguez' health improved. While the east wind generally brought rain, the west wind, descending from the plateau of Castile, brought heat in summer, and cold in winter, but it was always dry. Yet in general the old city was a comfortable place in which to live, and the ancient saying: "You would take Valencia for a piece of heaven on earth," was borne out at every season of the year.

Six months of his test at Valencia passed, and Brother Alonso Rodriguez was told that his religious life was to be continued in another sphere of activity. This was the Jesuit house at Palma, on the Island of Majorca, a possession of Spain, lying directly off her west coast, a terrain of singular beauty and charm.

While in the College of St. Paul, Alonso had enjoyed many singular privileges in the meeting with saintly and heroic souls who were following the standard of Father Ignatius Loyola.

One, the most unforgettable, came during the visit of a future martyr of the Company to the College. This was Father Ignatius Azevedo. He had come to Valencia from Rome, to seek volunteers for the foreign missions. Two members of the Company in the College offered themselves as his companions. One whose services he sought was Brother Juan of Majorca, the sacristan of the College, who was a good artist. Father Azevedo was happy to have in his possession, when he departed, a likeness of the Madonna of St. Luke, which the Brother had painted.

On July 15, 1570, Father Azevedo and his volunteers, thirty-eight in number, won the coveted palm of martyrdom. They were thrown into the sea. As he sank, wounded, to his death, Father Azevedo clung to the picture of our Lady he had received from Brother Juan.

Two of the Jesuits at Valencia were to conduct Brother Alonso Rodriguez to his new home at Palma, Majorca. They were Fathers Matthias Borrasa and Bernard Crespin. Father Borrasa, a native of Majorca, had just made his Solemn Profession of the four vows in the College of St. Paul.

So, once more, Brother Alonso Rodriguez bade farewell to a spot greatly endeared to his generous heart. With the two priests, he embarked for the place of his future work.

The dark blue domes, the thatched cottages of the peasantry, and the winding streets grew dim on the horizon as the vessel carried him from Valencia, which the Arabs had called bu-tarab – City of Joy.

V

AS BROTHER Alonso Rodriguez watched the shoreline of his homeland fading in the shadowy distance, something seemed to tell him that he would never see it again. Segovia, Valencia – he had loved but not lost them. In both the old walled cities there were souvenirs always to be cherished. He prayed to be worthy of them.

As the vessel carrying the three Jesuits bore eastward toward the city of Palma, the pleasant shores of Deya came into view, with great rocks on either side of the bay. Thence the course lay toward Cape Grosser and La Draginera to the left, and Santa Ponsa, a short distance ahead. At Santa Ponsa Don Jaime I had landed in December, 1229, and fought the great battle which resulted in the conquest of Majorca for the Christian arms.

The lovely Bay of Palma was entered between two jagged capes. Then came Fort Carlos, with its ancient Moorish signal tower of Porti Pi. This fort was likewise a souvenir of the gallant Don Jaime, and had been built by his order in 1229.

From a wooded height, the stalwart castle of Bellver towered above the little summer villa of Terreno, with the suburb of Santa Catalina in the foreground.

As he stood with Fathers Borrasa and Crespin on the deck of the vessel, Brother Alonso Rodriguez caught his first glimpse of the old city which was to be his new and permanent home.

Palma, very Oriental in aspect, had many steeples, like minarets—rising from its mosquelike edifices. Its flat-roofed white houses by the waterside seemed to squat, like pale sea birds, on the shimmering water. Close to the quay, the Gothic cathedral with many flying buttresses, and pinnacled towers, dominated all.

Removing his cap, Brother Alonso Rodriguez saluted his divine Lord for the first time on the Island of Majorca.

The inner bay was small but very sheltered and secure. As the Jesuits stepped on shore, they started at once to follow one of the narrow tortuous streets leading up from the sea.

The houses were generally low, three-storied structures, with the upper story, called a porche, having broad projecting eaves. Carefully terraced lawns and gardens receded from the front paths, which were cool, and shaded by many graceful palms. The pavements were uneven, but scrupulously clean. The sun looked down from serene blue heavens, and a fresh sea breeze filtered through the streets and lanes.

Brother Rodriguez followed the two priests through some of these streets, in places so narrow that signs had been affixed to them, bidding the pedestrian walk carefully. Mule-drawn wagons passed, their drivers reverently saluting the Jesuits. The muleteers addressed them in a tongue unfamiliar to Brother Rodriguez, but he noticed that Father Borrasa understood it. It was Majorcan, a remnant of the ancient Argonese, resembling Catalan, but softer than the pronunciation in use in Barcelona.

The College of Our Lady of Mount Sion, Montesion, was situated on a lofty elevation, overlooking the lower city and bay. As Brother Rodriguez climbed the ascent, behind his companions, the view of the sea and the surrounding countryside became more impressive and majestic.

At this time, the College of Montesion was a makeshift structure. Before the coming of the Jesuits to Palma, the viceroy and his wife, and the bishop of Palma, had been very anxious to have a house of the Company in the city. Through their efforts a small endowment was raised, and the superiors of the Company had agreed to make the foundation.

On August 24, 1650, three Fathers and three lay brothers had arrived. They were warmly welcomed by the canon priest, Juan Abrines, and their wants cared for.

At once, the Fathers began to look about for a house which would be suited to their purpose. They decided that the little Chapel of Our Lady of Mount Sion and the houses adjoining it could be utilized for the foundation.

It was believed that the new college and residence occupied the site of an early Jewish synagogue, used as a place of instruction for the converted Moors, after the capture of the Island by King Jaime. A noble lady, Isabel de Pinos, a member of a Christian family which had participated in the conquest, had later endowed it, so that an embryo college might be opened for a small number of students.

To the great satisfaction of the first Jesuits who reached Palma, the authorities, with the approval of the viceroy and the bishop, made over the little chapel to the Company. Several of the adjacent houses were purchased, a porter's lodge prepared, and the buildings fitted up as a religious residence and a day school or college.

The location of Montesion was very healthful, and it afforded a glorious view on all sides. A little to the east, the city gate of Del Campo led into the meadows and fields. To the south, was the monastery of St. Clare set in the midst of radiant gardens and crowned by stately palms, looking out on the glittering bay, with its shipping and bright headlands. To the west, was the cathedral and the principal section of the city, with the glorious mountains rising in the distance. To the north, the great Gothic Church of St. Eulalia, the Martyr Patroness of Barcelona, in which parish Montesion was located, could be seen, also the Church of San Francisco, with magnificent cloisters.

The first Jesuits on the spot had found in the little chapel a reredos, dating from the fifteenth century, having lovely representations of the Blessed Virgin and some of the Saints. They had also discovered a bell, hanging in the tower; a few old vestments, and a poor chalice of silver.

In September, 1561, the Blessed Sacrament had been solemnly installed in this little chapel. The community of six Jesuits then took up residence in the house, which had been renovated for their use. The year previous to the coming of Fathers Borrasa and Crespin and Brother Alonso Rodriguez to Palma, the second rector of Montesion, Father Bartolome Coch, a native of Majorca, had enlarged the house, to permit three classes in grammar to be opened within it.

Brother Rodriguez received the same heartfelt welcome accorded to his priest-companions as he met the community at Montesion for the first time. It comprised Father Lopez, the rector; Fathers Cusloa, Bru, Pardo, Bollicher, Jerome and Aguirre; Masters Duarte, Castell and Diego Morales, and the Lay Brothers, Morey, Navarro, Messeguer, Fortuny and Ruiz. Father Bartolomé Coch was about to succeed Father Lopez as rector at this time.

Brother Alonso Rodriguez was to share the religious life and labors of the devoted lay brothers in the little group, and to exercise himself, according to his holy rule, in whatever charge the superiors assigned to him.

After paying a visit to his Sacramental Lord in the little chapel, and being shown his room in the ramshackle building, Alonso was conducted to the kitchen and introduced to his first companion in labor, Brother Diego Ruiz, the Brother Cook.

Brother Ruiz had come to Palma the previous year. He was very happy in his life and work, and he speedily initiated the new Brother into the ways and customs of the house, and of this very important department of the community service.

To Alonso, Brother Ruiz seemed to be the perfect exemplar of the rules of the Company with special reference to lay brothers. Alonso had carefully studied the "Rules Of The Cook," and those pertaining to the other offices of the house. Now he had the opportunity to share in these offices, whose performance left the priests more at leisure to work directly for souls.

Alonso noticed that Brother Diego Ruiz was very careful to see that everything in the kitchen, the utensils, the food, the towels, and all else, was perfectly clean, and kept in good order. The Brother Cook showed Alonso how to dress the meats and vegetables, after carefully cleansing them, also how to prepare food for the sick. He acquainted him with the time for the serving of meals at the first and second tables, and told him what portions to serve to each member of the community.

Exceedingly jealous of his vow of poverty, Brother Ruiz took special care to apportion the fuel for the fire only as needed, and to watch the fires diligently. He took charge of all the food brought back from the tables after the meals, and if some of it could be again used in the house, he carefully set it aside. A certain portion was reserved for the poor, who invariably waited at the gates of every religious house, asking for food.

Alonso noted that Brother Ruiz kept the accounts relating to the purchase and dispensation of food, fuel, and so on, in a little notebook. He jotted down every item with great circumspection and taught Alonso how to keep this record.

Soon Alonso found that the Brother Cook, after fulfilling every duty of his charge most perfectly, was wont to disappear and not be seen about the corridors or rooms for some time each morning, in fact, from dawn on. He learned that Brother Ruiz cherished a wonderful devotion to the Holy Sacrifice of the Mass. Each morning the Brother Cook rose earlier than the community, so that he might start his work in the kitchen in good time to permit him to assist at several Masses before breakfast.

The new Brother was much pleased to have some share in the duties of Brother Diego Ruiz, who was a most faithful religious and on whom the superiors placed every reliance.

Sometimes Brother Rodriguez was assigned to the refectory, to assist the refectorian. In this department, as in the kitchen, all was supposed to be kept in good order and spotlessly clean. Water for the washing of hands, and towels to wipe them, were to be ready on a side table. The priests had separate towels, and all linen was changed twice weekly. Table cloths were cared for with the utmost diligence, and the refectorian and his assistants kept strict account of every piece of linen which came to the refectory and every piece which left it.

Brother Rodriguez was given the task of sharpening the knives, among other duties. The refectorian was delighted with this grave spiritual man. He knew that Brother Rodriguez had been a wool merchant, in Segovia, before entering the Society, and that he was used to giving orders, instead of receiving them. But now he asked only to be useful in whatever way the superiors disposed.

Sometimes Alonso rang the little bell which called the community to first and second tables. He took care to ring on the minute assigned, as soon as he had learned from Brother Ruiz that all was in readiness for serving. Sometimes he gathered up the food left after meals, and carried it to the Brother Cook, not allowing a crumb to disappear. He was never happier than when he was allowed to go to the gate and distribute some of this food to the poor.

He learned to write down in a small book kept for the purpose the names of the religious of the house who would be at home for meals, and any who would be out, so that Brother Ruiz could arrange for the number to be served at table. He swept the refectory after every meal and did whatever else was given him to do with such alacrity and good will that his superiors believed his charity and obedience would bring a special blessing on all the community. Occasionally he assisted the stone masons employed on the new church, and also helped the sacristan.

Brother Alonso Rodriguez loved and reverenced every duty assigned to him in his religious life. His hour of morning meditation, however, afforded him the greatest solace, as the source of spiritual strength for each succeeding day.

Sensing that, while the superiors rejoiced at his contentment, they sometimes feared that his frail health would not permit him to remain in the Company, the fears which had formerly oppressed him now returned. With them came scruples, lest he cherished some affection for the pleasures of the life he had renounced. Sometimes it seemed to him that all was lost; that his life in the Company was threatened by these violent interior troubles.

Humbly and diffidently he confided them to his confessor. The prudent priest strengthened him by reminding him that the greatest saints had suffered similarly, and had emerged victorious over the conflicts. All that mattered was that he should cling closely to God, and, while hating the evil, accept the suffering as allowed by the divine permission.

Although this counsel greatly helped, the trials continued, with Alonso's fervor keeping pace with them. Sometimes the anguish and fear were succeeded by great consolations, when it seemed that he was borne aloft to the very throne of God.

The superiors watched carefully over the spiritual development of this extraordinary Brother, of whom the Provincial, Father Cordeses, had made such an amazing prophecy. In Father Coch, who soon succeeded as rector of Montesion, he found a most helpful and understanding friend.

Father Coch bided the time, and when the day arrived for Brother Alonso Rodriguez to make his first simple Vows in the Company, he prepared to receive them with great joy and satisfaction.

On the second Sunday after Easter, April 5, 1573, kneeling in the little community chapel, at the feet of this good superior, the devoted Brother pronounced the words which bound him more closely still to his divine Lord in the Company of Jesus:

"Almighty, everlasting God, I, Alonso Rodriguez, though altogether most unworthy of Thy divine sight, yet trusting in Thy Goodness and Infinite Mercy, and moved with a desire of serving Thee, vow before the most sacred Virgin Mary, and the whole court of Heaven, to Thy Divine Majesty, perpetual Poverty, Chastity, and Obedience, in the Company of Jesus, forever to lead my life therein, understanding all things according to the Constitutions of the same Company. Therefore, I most humbly beseech Thee, by Thy Infinite Goodness and Mercy, by the Blood of Jesus Christ, that Thou wilt vouchsafe to admit this holocaust in an odor of sweetness, and that, as Thou hast already given me grace to desire and offer it, so Thou wilt also bestow plentiful grace on me to fulfill it. Amen."

On this happy day, Brother Alonso Rodriguez experienced the most perfect happiness of his life so far. As he received the congratulations of the community, he realized that his most fervent hopes were now fulfilled. Now he belonged to the Company, and the fear that he might be sent away as one unworthy grew dim.

In his prayers for perseverance, he recommended himself to the man who had planted the seed of his vocation in his heart, Father Peter Faber, first priest of the Society. This great man had expired peacefully in Rome, in the presence of Father Ignatius Loyola, on the Feast of St. Peter's Chains, Sunday, August 1, 1546. He had left, in his own hand writing a *Memorial*, of which a copy was now in every house of the Society. The first entry had been made the year of his blessed death. In it he spoke of the trials that may come to those who serve God. He had also indicated his great desire that the unfaithful everywhere might be brought to the knowledge and love of Jesus Christ, through the efforts and sacrifices of missionaries of his beloved Company:

"Many are stretching out their arms toward us; let us hasten to help them. The blood of martyrs calls to us to win the salvation of those amongst them and for whose salvation they were slain. And thus may God grant that one day some of the Company may have the opportunity and means of helping them."

Brother Alonso Rodriguez was aware that the work of the foreign missions was very dear to the heart of his illustrious Founder. In July, 1557, the Father General, Ignatius, had followed Father Peter Faber into eternity, leaving behind him a magnificent record of apostolic achievement. In his own lifetime, Ignatius had cherished the hope and desire of going to Africa, but this had not been possible. Instead, he had sent forth many of his noble-souled sons to far distant countries, to sweat and shed their blood in martyrdom for the souls of poor pagans.

Alonso had heard some of the older Fathers say that, although Father Peter Faber inspired those who met him by his sweetness and purity of soul, and by his great learning, when afterward they met Ignatius, Faber seemed no more than a child, such was the grandeur of appeal and personal magnetism of the holy founder. Ignatius of Loyola had loved God and souls as few men have loved them. To his last yearning cry: *"Ay, Dios!"* "Ah, God!" he had labored, suffered and planned for their salvation.

In his own little community Brother Alonso Rodriguez daily witnessed the rare virtues and achievements of those who bore witness to their allegiance to their Founder by following in his blessed footsteps. Not the least of these men of God was Father

Coch, his rector at Montesion. Father Coch had taught Alonso the practice of paying a little visit to the Blessed Sacrament every time he was about to leave the house, as well as the last thing before retiring at night.

On his part, Father Coch decided that the lowly servitor who had formerly been an influential wool merchant in Segovia, was striding rapidly toward the fulfillment of the prophesy made by the saintly Provincial, Father Cordeses:

"I intend that he shall be a saint, and a great one, and he will give great glory to the Company."

VI

NOW and then a member of the Company of Jesus, coming from Segovia to Palma, recalled to the mind of Brother Alonso Rodriguez the carefree and wholesome family life he had enjoyed in a period that now seemed long ago. When these thoughts came, he resolutely put them from him, and turned with renewed zest and purpose to the life he had chosen, a life of prayer, sacrifice, and consecrated labor. Happily, he was conscious of no dark shadow on the canvas of that past.

One of the professors at the College of Montesion who was deeply interested in the progress of Brother Alonso Rodriguez was Father Juan Aguirre, Prefect of Studies. Father Aguirre, a native of Toledo, had also been a married man in the world. On the death of his wife, in 1506, he had entered the Company of Jesus, coming to Majorca in 1568.

Father Aguirre was an exemplary religious and an excellent teacher and prefect. But he was nervous and inclined to scrupulosity. Father Aguirre found great consolation in speaking with Alonso, and entertained a high esteem for his character and spiritual endowment.

This appreciation on the part of the Jesuit priest was heightened considerably during a conversation held at table, when the Community were speaking about recollection in God.

Father Aguirre had proposed a question which aroused a lively discussion among the religious during the spiritual conference. This was whether it was possible for anyone to remain continually in the presence of God.

Several of the Fathers gave their opinion on the matter. The rector affirmed that he did not believe it was possible for anyone to keep himself absolutely, and without cessation, in that holy presence. The most one could do, he believed, was to refer to the divine majesty all the actions he might perform by purifying his intention. This was a kind of perpetual union with God, he thought.

Father Aguirre was not completely satisfied with this interpretation. Soon afterward, he met Brother Alonso Rodriguez, and he asked him what he thought about the matter.

With characteristic forthrightness and simplicity, Alonso answered: "To say that one cannot keep always in the presence of God is true, if we consider merely the power of man. But with the Divine assistance and grace, I would say that it is not merely possible, but sweet and easy."

Father Aguirre was impressed by the reply. He wanted to learn how Alonso himself practiced this union, and he continued:

"Let us appeal from experience, Brother. Tell me, from your own life, are you always in the presence of God? Or, if not, how long are you absent from it in the course of a day?"

Alonso reflected for a moment. He wished to be sure that God would be pleased with him if he disclosed his interior to Father Aguirre. He felt that He would, so he said:

"It seems to me, Father, for the time employed in reciting the *Credo,* or so."

Father Aguirre was edified, although not greatly surprised by the answer. When he spoke to the other Fathers about the incident, they agreed with him, that God was leading their Brother Rodriguez to great heights.

One of these Jesuits already knew what Alonso had told Father Aguirre, although he could not mention it. This was the superior. According to the rule, Alonso was accustomed to make a manifestation of his conscience at stated intervals to him. He had told the superior that, even when speaking with others, he did not lose sight of God. He had begun the practice of interior union when he entered the Company, at Valencia.

Father Aguirre soon had reason to know that Brother Rodriguez possessed great power to help him in his scrupulous state of mind.

One day, while Alonso was serving his Mass, the priest accidentally dropped the Sacred Host to the floor. Father Aguirre did not tell Alonso, afterward, that he was suffering great mental distress because of it. But Alonso knew that this was so. He prayed for his friend, asking God to comfort him and give him peace of mind.

Several days later, Alonso was again serving Mass for the priest in the community chapel. As the Holy Sacrifice went on, suddenly the humble Brother saw in a vision our divine Lord tenderly embracing Father Aguirre.

As soon as the Mass was over, he hurried to the rector and told him what he had seen. He begged him to tell Father Aguirre about the vision, so that he might be comforted and assured of God's good pleasure in his life.

The rector did so. When the unhappy Father Aguirre heard the story, all his peace of mind and heart was restored, and the scruple did not return to harass him.

The prudent rector, Father Coch, now serving his second term as rector of Montesion, had succeeded Father Matthias Borrasa, who had also been very kind to Alonso. Father Coch thought that it would be well to send Brother Alonso Rodriguez outside more often, in order to give him a little change of scene and air. He thought that Father Aguirre, also, would benefit by a little change.

He called the priest to him and told him that he was going

to send him to Spain for a little visit, and that he might take Brother Rodriguez with him as far as Soller, the port of embarkation.

Both Father Aguirre and Alonso were happy to be companions on the first lap of the journey.

The Bay of Soller was situated some twenty miles from Palma, facing Barcelona. The voyage to Spain from Soller was safer than that of the more direct route, also much shorter.

The road from Palma to Soller ran along in a nearly straight line for about nine miles. The mule-drawn wagon which carried the two Jesuits followed a wide plain where wheat, almonds, carobs and olives grew in luxuriance. The sight of the carob trees, bearing the pods which contained the sweet-flavored beans, recalled to Alonso his early novitiate days at Valencia, and he blessed God that he had been permitted to continue in the Company.

A little beyond the cultivated fields was a small village of houses, called Alfaba. Its gateway had an ancient Moorish roof, with an inscription in Arabic. This gate also renewed old memories in the heart of the humble Brother, for there were many similar gates and inscriptions in Segovia. It also reminded him of the archway of the gallery that ran about the Capilla Mayor, the principal chapel, of the Cathedral at Palma.

From this point on the road ascended in loops until the travelers were carried to the highest point of the pass. Looking backward over the plain, toward Palma and the sea, the mountains seemed to watch them, with the Puig Mayor, more than four thousand feet high, dominating the others.

As the path descended to the opposite side of the pass the white ribbon of roadway wound among olive vineyards, hemmed in by huge masses of rock.

From here the villages of Soller and Fonalutz could be seen. The landscape became more and more beautiful, with its wealth of luxuriant verdure. Soon the orange and lemon groves began, flooding the valley with fragrance.

Over pleasant roads the Jesuits entered the village of Soller, its white-walled houses having shutters of blue. They found lodging for the night in the house of the parish priest, who welcomed them with brotherly cordiality.

The vessel on which Father Aguirre was to embark would not sail until the following evening. After a quiet night and a pleasant day with their kind host, Father Aguirre and Brother Alonso Rodriguez started off to the port, walking the two and one half miles over a good road. Having time on his hands, Father Aguirre proposed to Alonso that they should climb the flight of steps leading from the port up to the main section of the town.

Alonso gladly acquiesced in the proposal. He found the ascent difficult in his frail state of health, but he said nothing of this to his friend. When the two reached the top, they could look afar off to a village called Muleta, where some important copper and silver mines were located. In another direction, about two miles from the village of Soller, was a wild gorge. Father Aguirre told Alonso that in the vicinity of this gorge there was a monastery called Lluch, where young boys were trained in singing.

The port of Soller was set within a pretty bay, guarded at its narrow entrance by twin beacons. The two Jesuits were standing there, awaiting the time for Father Aguirre to go on board the vessel, employing the time in reciting the rosary to ensure a favorable journey for the priest.

As he was following the prayers and mysteries, Alonso heard a voice speaking to him. It was that of the Blessed Virgin. She told him that if Father Aguirre should sail in that vessel, he would be taken captive by Moorish corsairs.

Trembling all over his frail being, not daring to look at his companion, Alonso said to the Lady: "O, my Queen! If they take him prisoner, I will never leave you alone until you yourself bring him back to my cell!"

Instantaneously, the wind changed. It became evident that

the vessel could not possibly sail before the following morning.

Father Aguirre was extremely puzzled by this change in the weather. A moment before, a brisk wind had promised his immediate embarkation. Now it was impossible for the vessel to leave port.

Alonso did not speak to Father Aguirre of the voice he had heard. His heart was filled with gratitude to her who had saved his dear friend from a dreadful fate, and he employed the time in thanking her, again and again.

The parish priest of Soller had known that a number of Moorish vessels were a little way out at sea. He had not wished to frighten Father Aguirre by telling him about this. So he had written a letter to the rector of Montesion, telling him to recall Father Aguirre before he should sail.

Although Soller lay seventeen miles distant from Palma, the letter had reached the College the evening of the day it was mailed.

When Father Coch received it, he immediately sought the advice of his brother Jesuits as to what he should do.

"Father Aguirre is still at Soller, and I am in doubt whether I should allow him to go on to Spain," he told them. "I leave the decision to the majority of you fathers."

The unanimous decision was that the priest should be told to return to Montesion, and abandon his trip. Father Coch immediately wrote him to that effect.

The rector's letter reached the house of the parish priest of Soller just as Father Aguirre and Brother Rodriguez were about to start again for the port. At the command of his superior, the Jesuit prepared to return to Palma. When he told Alonso of Father Coch's order, the former gave thanks to the holy Virgin for having exercised her loving protection over Father Aguirre. The return trip from Soller was made without delay.

Soon it became known all over Majorca that, at the hour when the priest and brother entered the college, the vessel, which had sailed, fell into the hands of the Algerines, at the very mouth of the port of Soller. Among the captives of the corsairs was a Dominican priest and the brother of one of the Jesuits at Montesion. These two men were forced into slavery by their masters, and spent many years in captivity.

Brother Alonso was thankful to be again at home in the College. While he deeply appreciated the kindness of Father Coch in sending him as companion to Father Aguirre, he cared little about outside excursions, and went out only when obedience commanded.

In the Fathers and scholastics of his community he found greathearted protectors and friends, and in the lay brothers of his own group, models of the virtues inculcated by their holy founder for those who served in the lowly but privileged capacity of temporal coadjutors.

Brother Diego Ruiz continued to edify Alonso by his unswerving devotion to the exacting duties of the kitchen, and by his great love for the Mass.

Brother Francis Morey, a stone mason by trade, a deformed brother, worked diligently on the renovating of the old, and the construction of the new parts of the house and college. Brother Juan Messeguer, the community carpenter, followed the trade of the humble St. Joseph, and of the divine Child of Nazareth, helping to make the community more comfortable by the labor of his hands.

The other lay brothers in the house were equally generous and devoted in their services, striving mightily to uphold the hands of their beloved rector, Father Bartolomé Coch, in his many and grave burdens.

Alonso knew, from the rector, that one of the community fathers, Father Matthias Borrasa, with whom he had come to Majorca, had wished to offer himself as a lay brother to the Company. Only on the orders of the superiors was he prevailed upon to study for the priesthood. The superiors had felt that his great talents of mind fitted him for the apostolate of teaching, whereas he had wished to spend his life in the more menial duties of the Company, where he felt there was an equal opportunity to give glory to God and aid to souls.

Meanwhile, the community at Montesion, a pioneer group, as all the other communities of Jesuits in Spain, followed from afar the triumphs of their beloved Company in various regions of the world.

Brother Alonso Rodriguez often thought of the lot of the lay brothers, who had been privileged to accompany these foreign missionaries of the Company of Jesus on their perilous but glorious ventures for Christ. Like his holy Founder, he would have given his all to go with them. But his weakened body, and the dispositions of his superiors, had made this quite out of the question. The most he felt he could do was to offer his prayers and sacrifices for the success of these selfless brothers in their living martyrdom, which often became actual martyrdom, as one after another was put to death by the poor pagans they sought to save.

Best of all, he believed that in the faithful adherence to his vow of obedience he could help these brethren in the Company and their poor clients, according to the rules of obedience set down by his founder:

> Wherefore, dear Brethren, lay aside wholly, as far as you can, your own wills; hand over freely and dedicate to your Creator in His ministers the freedom He Himself has bestowed upon you. Consider it no small advantage of your own free-will, that you are able to give it back fully, through Obedience, to Him from Whom you received it and by so doing, you not only do not lose, but rather increase and perfect it; since by this means you direct all your wills by that most certain rule of rectitude, the will of God, interpreted to you by him who governs you in the place of God.

VII

OFTEN Brother Alonso Rodriguez accompanied the fathers of Montesion on their visits to the sick or on other necessary business about Palma. All the priests of the community were glad to have as their companion this cheerful quiet-souled Brother, who was always ready to serve them. They had grown accustomed to ask his prayers in any need, whether of a spiritual or temporal nature. Alonso accepted these commissions in all simplicity, thinking that the other Brothers of the house were equally favored.

As he passed along the streets of the Majorcan capital he grew familiar with the landmarks which made it so picturesque and historic. When in the vicinity of the cathedral, he liked to visit the Royal Chapel, the oldest part of the sacred edifice, which had been built as a place of sepulture for the Majorcan sovereigns.

He had visited the Church of San Francisco, dedicated to his own patron Saint. It consisted of a single nave, splendidly enriched with the marbles of the Island and with the Valencian tiles so familiar to Alonso during his sojourn in Valencia. While his priest companion transacted some business with the spiritual sons of the Saint of Assisi, who had charge of the church, Alonso could stop at the tomb of St. Raymund, a special patron and glory of Majorca, and offer his prayers. St. Raymund had won the palm of martyrdom in 1235, in Algiers. His effigy, carved out of warm-toned marble, and surmounting the tomb, was singularly lifelike.

Bellver Castle, which Alonso had glimpsed from the vessel as he voyaged to Majorca, was a very important monument of an historic era in the life of the old city. At this time it belonged to Don Pedro de Pax, Procurator General of the Island, a member of the first nobility.

Because he was obliged to be away at court most of the time,

Don Pedro, a widower, had entrusted the charge of his four young daughters to his sister, Dona Jane de Pax, who resided with them in the castle. The noble Don knew that the children were safe in her care, and that, living in this secluded spot, they were removed from the dangers and distractions of the city.

Dona Jane was an invalid. Father Matthias Borrasa, of Montesion, was her confessor, and he was accustomed to visit her regularly, to hear her confession, celebrate Mass in the chapel of the house, and give her and the older girls holy Communion.

One day Father Borrasa asked Brother Alonso Rodriguez to accompany him to Bellver. Alonso was happy to do this, although he was aware that the ascent to the castle was steep, and at the time he was suffering from severe pains in his legs. He went for his cloak, and accompanied the priest out of the college.

The climb up the hill caused him great misery, but he did not speak of it to Father Borrasa. Also, the sun was piercing hot, its nearly perpendicular rays striking down on the hill and converting it into a veritable oven.

At the steepest part of the ascent, Alonso realized that he could go no farther. He was obliged to tell his companion of his predicament.

Father Borrasa instructed him to rest by the wayside for a while, then, if he felt able, to continue the walk and meet him at the castle.

Alonso sat down on a great stone, and Father Borrasa toiled on without him. He took out his beads and began the recitation of the rosary, following Father Faber's method of meditating on the holy mysteries of our Lord's life.

He had gone only a short way in the prayers of the first decade, looking out on the rooftops and turrets of the fine old city and the shimmering waters of the bay, lying warm in the tropical sun, when, suddenly, a lovely lady stood before him.

She, too, held a rosary. Over her head was a halo of light. Her face was very tender and pure, and her expression celestial.

Dumbfounded, overwhelmed with emotion, Alonso looked at her, not saying a word.

She looked on him approvingly, he thought. Then, before he had time to try to rise and fall to his knees, she came close. Taking a white cloth from her garment, she wiped his face with it, and spoke to him. He felt a cool refreshment, whereas his face had been hot with perspiration a moment before.

As he experienced this divinely soothing refreshment to his soul and body alike, Alonso started to thank the heavenly Queen, and ask her what she wished him to do.

But she had vanished, as suddenly as she had come.

Feeling a strange sense of lightness in his whole being, Alonso rose, and quickly began to climb the rest of the way to the castle of Bellver. All the stiffness and soreness had gone from his legs, and he was no longer conscious of any discomfort.

A servant admitted him to the castle. He sat down in an outer room, while Father Borrasa remained within, hearing Dona Jane's confession and counseling his noble penitent.

Meanwhile, the four young girls of the family gathered about Alonso, talking, all together, of their little amusements and interests.

As they did so, a flock of white doves, which had been circling about in the outer courtyard, entered through one of the arches. They began to move gently above Brother Alonso Rodriguez, who sat on a chair, meditating on the wonderful favor granted to him a little while before.

The little girls called to him that the doves were lighting on his head, his shoulders, and on his knees. But he did not seem to hear them, or to notice that the doves were there.

After a few moments, they flew off and did not return. But Brother Alonso Rodriguez did not know they had gone, or realize they had come in through the arch.

When Father Borrasa had finished his spiritual duties, he came out and bade Alonso accompany him to the chapel, and serve him during his Mass.

The children called out to the priest: "The doves! The doves!" But Father Borrasa did not know what they meant, and Alonso said nothing by way of explanation.

On the way back to Montesion, however, he told Father Borrasa about the apparition of the Lady. The priest listened, but did not make any reply. However, as soon as he reached the college, he went to find some of the other Fathers, to tell them what Alonso had narrated to him. All were of the opinion that the Mother of God had appeared to her favored son, Alonso, and that she had spoken to him, as he said.

Notwithstanding these favors, which increased as the months passed, Alonso continued to experience temptations and interior trials which caused him acute anguish of soul.

One day he appeared before his confessor with a large scroll of paper in his hand. The priest saw that there was much writing on the scroll.

"What is this?" he asked Alonso. "What do you want to do, Brother?" He felt that he knew quite well what his penitent wanted to do.

"To make a general confession, Father," Alonso replied. "I have taken all possible pains to prepare for it, and I think that when I have made it, it will set all my scruples at rest."

"But did you not take all possible pains in your former confessions?" his confessor questioned.

Alonso was forced to admit that he had done so.

"Well, then," said the priest, "put this idea out of your head. Tear up that paper and make an ordinary confession."

Alonso tore the paper to shreds, and made his confession as usual. From that confession on he was never again troubled by scruples as to former ones.

However, the faithful Brother continued to suffer from trials of spiritual abandonment. A sense of his own guilt was always present in his heart, and he felt that he was a great sinner, who had no cause to feel any hope for deliverance.

"I feel like a glass tossed among rocks, Father," he told the confessor one day. "But my trust in God has never failed me."

These interior trials and his penances and vigils, as well as his unremitting work about the house, wore down Alonso's strength, until his frail condition alarmed his superiors. Even the students of the college noticed his worn condition; they called him, among themselves: *"Extremaunviado"* or *"Hermano oleado,"* meaning, "The Brother who has been anointed." Actually, Alonso had not been anointed, but to the young men he seemed like one nearly dead, as he moved about the house with slow unsteady step.

Father Coch intensified the previous efforts made to carry forward the construction of the new church. As a result of his efforts, a large part of the nave was completed at this time. It had four chapels on either side, affording great facility for all the priests of the community to say Mass there daily, without crowding one another. The new bishop of Palma, Juan Vique y Manrique, blessed the edifice on the eve of Trinity Sunday, and preached there on the following day.

Busy as he was with many pressing burdens and duties, Father Coch found time and energy to consider the condition of Alonso very carefully. He was anxious about the health of his beloved disciple. It occurred to him that a change of work might help his condition.

The post of Porter at a college such as Montesion was necessarily a very busy and important one. The brother who exercised it had many distractions in attending to the errands of the different callers who came to the college, including the clergy and many of the dignitaries and nobility of the city.

The post was given to Alonso by Father Coch, with every confidence on the part of the good rector that this brother would acquit himself of it with great satisfaction, and also with improvement to his health.

The opening of the new church had attracted many additional students to Montesion. The community now numbered twenty.

From the first, Brother Alonso Rodriguez served at the door with modesty, humility, cheerfulness and discretion. Soon the callers began to notice that he was a very unusual brother. No matter how his patience was tried, how hot or cold the weather might be, no one ever saw him show signs of impatience.

On one occasion, by mistake, Alonso happened to lock the church door for the night before one of the workmen, engaged on the construction, had left. Soon this man completed his task and was about to leave, when he found he could not.

He began to pound furiously on the church door.

Alonso heard the noise, and hurried to investigate. When he opened the door, the workman began to abuse him, with a tirade of opprobrious epithets.

Alonso listened meekly. When the man stopped, out of breath, Alonso humbly apologized for what he termed his want of thought. He soothed the outraged feelings of the workman with such gentle words, and with such a kindly manner, that the man was ashamed of his behavior, as well as astonished that the brother had failed to rebuke him for his insolence.

As he was leaving the premises through the courtyard, the workman met one of the Fathers, who had witnessed the incident. The workman said to him:

"That brother is not a man, he is an angel!"

Sometimes the students played tricks on the kindly Brother Porter. They would ring the doorbell, then run to hide, watching to see how Alonso accepted the inconvenience, when he opened the door. They never found him angry or excited on these occasions, nor did he afterward rebuke them for the trouble they had caused him. He received their shafts goodnaturedly, and was always pleasant to them when he met them, no matter what they might have done to tease him.

Alonso was very happy in his new post, and soon Father Coch was gratified to observe that his health began to improve a little.

For his conduct as Porter, Alonso composed a little set of rules, which he memorized and faithfully observed:

As soon as he heard the doorbell, he would instantly raise his heart to God, and say to Him:

"Lord, I must open to Thee, for love of Thee!"

Or, at the call of the bell, he would make acts of joy in his heart, and think that he was going to the door to open it to his God, as if God Himself were standing outside, and had rung. He would say, as he went to open the door:

"I am coming, my Lord!"

If he felt unusually exhausted, after a trying day at his post, he would make haste, just the same, when the call came.

If someone rang impatiently, even violently, and he should feel any interior irritation, he would instantly repress it, and calm himself. Then he would go to the door.

With an old scratchy pen, he had written:

"When summoned to the gate, act as though your God was coming in; open the door for Him, and receive Him. And if you are sent with a message, act as though it is God, not man, who sends you; and as it is God's business, you will dispatch it at once, with all joy and affection, as so good a Lord deserves, always inclining your will to His.

"When you have taken the message and are returning with the answer, consider that you are coming back to God, with all possible joy and love, and fix the eyes of your soul on God, as if you were speaking to Him, and not to man. And in this way, you must deliver the answer. And if anyone wants to go out, you must consider that you are opening the gate to your God, Who wants to go out, not to man. And with this feeling, joined with great signs of charity, and in all humility, open the gate, and so let him depart."

In January, 1580, Father Juan Poggia, a Majorcan, became rector.

The student body at Montesion had so greatly increased that he felt it necessary to increase the number of classrooms and to purchase a near-by house, formerly a synagogue, for the purpose. The municipality of Palma contributed generously to the enterprise. Father Poggia also purchased a country home, one mile from the city, as a place of rest and recreation for the community.

He named it Santa Maria, and it commanded a view of Palma and its queenly bay, also of the wide plain, sprinkled over with olive trees, and the pleasant farmlands. It had a spacious garden plot, which Father Poggia planted with vines and fruit trees of every species.

The new rector believed that this villa would promote the health and spirits of all the Jesuits at Montesion, and aid them in their arduous work. He remembered that his great founder had a very human understanding of the needs of men and that he had legislated to make their burdens as light as possible, so that their souls might fly, less hampered by earthly things, to realms of spiritual considerations.

The year 1580 brought to all the community at Montesion a great sorrow. Especially did it affect the little group of faithful lay brothers, since it removed from their midst Brother Juan Messeguer, the Catalan carpenter, who had performed a most useful service for the Company. Brother Messeguer had proved himself invaluable at Montesion in this period of its growth. He had aided in the work of building the new church and of renovating and enlarging the residence. Meanwhile, he had carried on all the duties and exercises of his religious life with great punctuality and good will. All the community realized that they would miss this thoroughly reliable servant of his divine Master, whose strong hands and obedient heart were ever at their call.

In the company of the fathers and brothers he had loved so dearly, Brother Messeguer was borne to his last rest in the little Chapel of Our Lady, on the epistle side of the main altar in the church of Montesion. Even in death, the community were to guard his mortal remains closely, in sacrifice and prayer. Close to his tomb, the Mass would be offered daily, and his name often recalled.

The months passed, and hardly had the pain of this loss been somewhat tempered when another blow struck into the ranks of the religious at the college, and another zealous lay brother went to his eternal rest.

In late August, just as the Community came down to the refectory for the midday repast, Father Coch hurried from the yard, his face white and stricken. He announced that Brother Juan Far, who had replaced Brother Messeguer in the carpentry work at Montesion, had fallen from the roof, where he had been working, and had been instantly killed.

All at Montesion believed that this good brother, also, had fully satisfied the prescriptions of his life in the Company. He had worked well and uncomplainingly, and now his labors in this world were finished.

On the morning of the day following Brother Far's passing, after the Requiem Mass, he was laid beside Brother Messeguer, beneath the mantle of the Holy Virgin, in her Chapel of the Assumption. As was customary in that day, in tropical countries, the funeral services were not delayed. All realized that the little community of the dead at Montesion was increasing. Who would be next? No one knew, but all felt more conscious than ever of the transitoriness of this life and the certainty of that which lies beyond.

Brothers Juan Messeguer and Juan Far were gone from the sight of their companions, but their memory was held sacred and precious. Those of their band who remained behind meditated anew, and with a new meaning, on the rules of the temporal coadjutors which Father General Ignatius Loyola had written out for the lay brothers of his Company:

"All ought to understand that their foremost intention ought to be to serve the Divine Majesty in the Company, not only so as to employ themselves with all diligence in spiritual exercises, prayer, and devotion at the times appointed; but also to perform the household services of their calling, of whatever kind, however humble and menial they may be, with readiness to spend all their lifetime in them: persuading themselves that by so doing they serve and praise their Creator and Lord, for whose love and reverence they labor in them.

"Their chief care must be purity of conscience, and they are seriously to apply themselves to the study of those virtues which are the principal ornaments and perfection of this grade in the Company, and without which they cannot in any way rise to the dignity of the state to which they are called – such as devotion, quietness of soul, manageableness, love of virtue, desire of perfection; that they may give edification to the community and to externs and, being content with the lot of Martha, employ themselves in the active life; embracing with special love the Institute of the Company, of which they should strive to become useful members to the glory of the Lord."

Brother Alonso Rodriguez deemed that he alone, of all the brothers, living and dead, at Montesion, failed to reach this standard, inculcated by the rules of the founder. His yearning desire and prayer was that he might learn to measure up to it, and become an exemplar of the virtues of which he believed his dead confreres were a shining light.

As Brother Rodriguez had looked for the last time in this world on the still face of Brother Juan Far, reposing in a little room of the residence, he had realized still more how great and glorious were his privileges as Temporal Coadjutor. The great wound on the dead Brother's head could not detract from the peace and majesty of his countenance. His strong hands, inured to rough tools, were quite filled with the rosary and crucifix. Like St. Joseph, the carpenter of Nazareth, he had laid them down for all time. In death the lowly brother seemed far nobler than in life, and the worn habit seemed to cling to his gaunt form, as if to embrace him.

Brother Diego Ruiz continued to hold his post in the kitchen. Sometimes, when he had a little respite from his duties at the door, Alonso paid him a visit, and took a hand at washing or peeling the fruits and vegetables, or went over, with Diego, the items recorded in the little order book.

Soon an occupation exceptionally pleasing to the Brother Porter was assigned to him. This was the instruction in their catechism of some of the little children of noble family, and others, in Palma. He could easily attend to it while he sat on his stool in the Porteria, awaiting the next summons of the doorbell. He loved children, and the sight of these little ones, brought to him by their servants, or older brothers and sisters, reminded him of his own three little angels, Garcia, Maria, and Alonso. He thought that the child-trinity would be pleased to see him occupied in such a task, the very same that his Blessed Lord had undertaken during His missionary career upon earth.

The superiors were well satisfied when they saw Alonso, seated in the midst of his little charges, telling them about our Lord, His holy Mother, and the saints; hearing them recite their prayers in childish treble voices, and asking them questions from the little catechism.

Brother Rodriguez had also become a valuable recruiter of vocations to the Company and to other religious communities represented in the city. He sought and won vocations from among the students at the college and others who came to visit there, having heard of his holiness and wisdom. Father Poggia, the new superior, far from discouraging this, was much gratified over it. Soon there were so many aspirants for the Company that all could not be accepted. When possible, they were sent to Spain to make their novitiate.

When the students asked Alonso for some counsel for their lives, he frequently counseled them: "If you want God to give you what you ask, either for yourself or for anyone else, love Him ardently, and ask always for what is to His greatest glory. Love your neighbor and the welfare of your own soul, and be sure He will grant you all you need, for He loves us with an infinite love and knows what we need. So that, really, we hardly require to ask or wish for anything, but we can leave the care of ourselves to God, and so everything will go right."

Father Poggia noticed that whenever Brother Alonso Rodriguez served Mass in the church, the worshipers always surrounded the particular altar where he was. The different fathers used to ask that he might serve their Masses, because they experienced a great unction when he did so. Their request was granted, as far as could be.

At this time it was customary for the server at Mass to offer the communicants some water to drink, after they had received Holy Communion. When Brother Rodriguez officiated in this capacity it seemed to those kneeling at the altar rail that they were close to an angel, as some of them testified.

Fathers and Brothers knew that in the refectory their Brother Rodriguez was a model of mortification and penance. He was always quick to see that those nearest to him were served promptly and that they had every essential to the enjoyment of their meal. For himself, he chose the worst articles on the table and avoided those which would please the palate most. His table companions noticed that he never took salt, although they were aware that he had a special liking for it.

Rarely did any mishap in the services of the house occur to mar the perfection of order. Once, however, an incident took place which afforded Alonso a unique opportunity of satisfying his love of penance in the refectory.

The first dish of cooked gourds brought to the table was placed close to him. But the gourds happened to be very unpalatable, because they were bitter and unfit to serve. By some error this fact had escaped Brother Ruiz' notice when they were brought to the kitchen.

From the odor of the dish, Alonso knew that the gourds were bad. He immediately set aside some fruit he had taken, and helped himself to a portion of them.

A scholastic named Marimon, who was seated beside him, then took some. Alonso was already eating the gourds. But when Marimon had tasted the first mouthful, he found them so nasty in taste that he had to rinse his mouth with water. He called, quickly, to the others:

"Mors est in olla!" The table conversation was invariably carried on in Latin—by this exclamation, the scholastic meant to say that "Death is in the pot!" or "The gourds are poison!"

The rector ordered that the unsavory dish be removed at once. Just then he looked down to Alonso, and saw that he had not only eaten the gourds, but that he was scraping his plate, in order not to leave any remnants of them behind.

Father Poggia exchanged significant glances with one of the other fathers. No one said anything, however, about the matter. Brother Rodriguez had eaten the bad gourds, and the remainder of them had been carried away. All continued with the meal as before.

Once in awhile Alonso found himself the object of a little innocent jest, as the community amused themselves at his expense. This pleased him very much, for he thought that he was a little useful then, even if he was a fool.

One day at recreation the fathers, including some of the professors of the college, were discussing, in the presence of the lay brothers, the sport of swimming. Varied opinions were expressed in the matter. Some of the fathers thought that it should be discouraged among the students because it interfered with their studies. Others thought, according to the ideas prevalent in that day, that it was against modesty. Still others, more advanced in their enlightenment, declared that it was necessary to safeguard the students from danger, since they were living on an island.

Father Coch turned to Brother Rodriguez and asked him if he knew how to swim.

He replied: "Yes, Father, I do."

"Well, then, let us see how you do it."

Father Coch had not looked for so exact a response as Alonso gave. For the latter at once rose and threw himself on the floor. There he went through all the motions of a swimmer.

The priest said, hurriedly: "Get up, Brother! That will do!" From that time on, he was very careful not to ask Brother Rodriguez to do anything that might cause embarrassment to him or anyone else.

Sometimes the Brother Porter was allowed to visit the sick, who were under the care of the Jesuits, and carry them baskets of food and medicines. They were always cheered and happy when they saw the holy brother, whose kind and soothing words brought them great comfort and encouragement.

On such occasions, always before leaving the college, Alonso would say to his Lord: "Lord, if You see that I shall offend You while I am out, although I am going out under obedience, take away my life, for You alone are my Life, and I am resolved to suffer a thousand deaths rather than offend You, however slightly."

When he had reached the outer door, he would mark his name on the board as: "Out." Then he would take holy water, in the Sign of the Cross, repeating the words of the Psalm: "Show, unto me, O Lord, Thy ways, and teach me Thy paths."

The Jesuits at Montesion began to realize that God was pleased to work miracles through their Brother Alonso Rodriguez.

There was a resident of Palma named Juan Vivot, who, as he was pursuing a runaway slave, received a bullet wound in the arm. His physician declared that the wound was mortal. Juan prepared himself for the end. But he was in such pain that he begged the rector of Montesion to send Brother Rodriguez to him. He had met Alonso during his visits to the college and he had reason to think he was a saint.

Father Poggia complied with Vivot's request. He sent Alonso, with one of the Fathers. While the priest was giving the Sacraments to the wounded man in his chamber, Alonso sat in an outer room.

When the priest came out, he requested Alonso to take his place in the chamber.

Alonso obeyed. As soon as he reached the bedside he assured Vivot that he would not die, but would recover.

He talked further with him, but when Vivot asked him to make the Sign of the Cross over his wounded arm, he modestly declined to do this. Just then the priest returned to the room. Hearing Vivot make the request, he bade Alonso comply with it.

Alonso then made the Sign of the Cross over the wounded arm, and also laid his hand upon the wound.

As soon as he did so, the pain in the arm grew much less severe. Vivot tried to move it, and found that he could do so, although it had been paralyzed since the shooting.

A few days later, the physician declared the wounded man to be completely out of danger.

As soon as he was able to visit Montesion, Vivot went there and thanked Alonso for what he had done. Under his guidance he began a course of instruction on the spiritual life.

Without any realization of his own merits, Alonso continued to help those who applied for his aid, after receiving permission to do so from the superior. In the meantime, taking careful heed to what he deemed his grave imperfections, he wrote in a little notebook, his *Vade Mecum* of the spirit, what he felt and thought:

Whenever you do anything, you must offer it to God, at the beginning, in the middle, and at the end.

At the beginning, undertake it only to please our Lord, out of holy obedience. While in the midst of it, you must unite it to the life, labors, death and merits of Jesus Christ. When finished, offer it to God for your soul's salvation, and for your own special needs, and beg Him to accept it for this end.

When you wait on table, you must place yourself, first of all, in the presence of God, for whose love you are going to do that duty, in order to please Him in the person of those you are serving, and because holy obedience commands it. While you are waiting on the community, be very careful to lift your heart to God, and say often: "Lord, I unite this action with the life, passion, labors and death of Jesus Christ, Thy only Son."

When you have finished, say with new fervor: "I offer Thee, my God, this work purely for Thy glory, for my soul's salvation, to relieve the Souls in Purgatory, and for the conversion of sinners and heretics."

You must take great pains to please God, and to give Him satisfaction in everything, never desiring anything which is not allowed, no matter how trivial it may be.

When you have anything to say, when you wish to look at anything, or to eat anything at table, whatever, in fact, you do, you must, in your heart, ask God's leave beforehand, and if your conscience has nothing against it, you can then do what you judge conformable to His Will; but never act in any other way.

You must have no other thought in what you do but to please God by a pure intention, for He Himself has no other end in everything but His glory.

In conclusion, you must live as if you saw nothing, heard nothing, felt nothing, and as if you were already dead to all your senses, and sought in everything the honor and glory of God, in the fulfillment of His Will, and nothing else.

Brother Alonso Rodriguez had advanced a long way from the days of his childhood in the yellow house on the Plaza del Azoquejo.

VIII

THE little cell in the Jesuit residence at Montesion assigned to Brother Alonso Rodriguez never held any object that might give pleasure to the senses or sensibilities. Brother Rodriguez loved flowers and he admired them on the altars and at the shrines of our Lady and the saints. But he was never seen to pick one in the luxuriant gardens of the college patio, or to breathe in its fragrance. Grapes grew in abundance on the premises. But Brother Rodriguez never took one from the vines. He was most solicitous, however, that the other members of the community should enjoy these simple pleasures, which he believed they deserved because of their virtues and accomplishments.

In March, 1585, Brother Rodriguez pronounced his Final Vows as Temporal Coadjutor in the Company of Jesus. His cup of happiness was now full. Nothing remained but to go forward in the path marked out for him by his glorious founder.

As time went on, he continued to serve occasionally in the

kitchen or refectory, finding in each object he touched some reminder of the Creator's goodness and bounty.

When he carried in dishes to the table, he behaved as if he was performing service for royalty, and he was humbly subservient to all.

While waiting for the community to come down to table, he would say, over again, to his Divine Lord: "Lord, I unite this action with the life, labors, passion, and death of Jesus Christ, Thy only Son." When he had finished his appointed task he would say: "I offer Thee, my God, this work purely for Thy glory; for my soul's salvation; to relieve the souls in Purgatory, and for the conversion of heretics."

Father Poggia, like his predecessor in the rectorship of the college, Father Coch, had reason to think that Alonso was deemed eccentric, or extreme in his interpretation of the rule, by some. Yet even the few Jesuits who did not thoroughly comprehend his holiness were forced to think that the wonders worked through his prayers were very real, and very extraordinary.

Calling Alonso to him, one afternoon, Father Poggia told him that he was to go with another Father on a sick call to a citizen of Palma who lay dangerously ill.

Alonso thought it a great favor to go with one who carried the Blessed Sacrament with him. The two Jesuits walked through cool streets to a part of the city where persons of no particular note lived in humble abodes. Alonso recalled that he had heard how a king had visited such a poor cottage in Palma, and, after partaking of a repast such as only the poor could offer, said to his host: "I have dined well." Now the divine King was coming to visit one of His own, carried by a member of the Company upon which He had bestowed so many favors as a sign of His good pleasure. With the priest was a lay brother, whose marvelous piety and zeal had brought rich blessings upon his community and the house in which he lived.

Alonso, quite ignorant of his perfection, recited his prayers in silence as he walked beside his friend. When the two entered the house of the sick man, as usual, he sat down in an outer room and continued his devotions, while the father went in to the sick.

The priest had just placed his purple stole about his shoulders and was preparing to listen to the confession of the patient, when the latter began to rave in delirium. Nothing could be done for him while he was in that condition.

Realizing that it was not even safe for him to remain in the room alone with the man, the priest left the chamber and joined Alonso.

"Brother," he told him, "I wish you would pray with me that this poor man may be restored to his senses. I don't want to see him die without the Sacraments, and right now he is stark mad."

Alonso began to pray for the man, his head resting on his breast and his hands joined in fervent supplication. He asked God to have pity on the poor man and give him back his senses, in order that he might make his peace with Him and die in His grace.

When the prayer was finished, the priest returned to the inner room.

To his joy, and some surprise, he found the man quite calm and rational, and waiting to make his confession.

Back in the college, the confessor acquainted Father Poggia with what had occurred in the little cottage. Father Poggia saw in the incident a further evidence of the power of Alonso with heaven. He told the priest: "We have had a hard time to keep our Brother Rodriguez here at Montesion, Father. All the houses of our Order in Spain are asking us to send him to them for awhile, so that they, also, may share in the blessings of his presence. But I think there is much work for him to do in Majorca."

Father Juan Aguirre, whom Alonso had helped to overcome scruples by his prayers, was reported to be very ill in Gandia, where he had gone from Montesion. Father Poggia learned that this good priest had fallen into a state of religious melancholy bordering on insanity. This was the worst form of mental disorder. Father Aguirre had lost all hope of his salvation, and no member of the Jesuit faculty with whom he lived seemed able to arouse him from his depression. His rector even feared he would die without the Sacraments.

No one at Montesion happened to mention this to Alonso. But, as he was walking along a dim passage in the residence, removed from the bustle of the students, and wrapped in recollection, a voice broke the silence, although no human being was in sight, or near at hand.

The voice, which seemed to come out of the air, said to Alonso:

"Pray for your friend, Father Aguirre, who is in great danger."

Startled, but very eager to help his friend, Alonso began to pray to the Blessed Virgin. He offered through her blessed hands all his acts of penance, his Communions, and other works of piety for the beloved priest. He continued to do this until something seemed to assure him that Father Aguirre would be quite well.

Several months later, the Provincial of Aragon, Very Reverend Jerome Roca, came to Montesion. When Alonso was giving him an account of his conscience, he told him about the message he had received, and what he had done in response to it.

Father Roca, taken by surprise, at once told Alonso all that had taken place at Gandia in relation to Father Aguirre. The priest had recovered his health instantaneously, and when the Provincial had last seen him, he was going about his usual tasks in peace of mind and health of body. This had happened at the very time the voice had spoken to Alonso.

The religious life of Alonso Rodriguez as a member of the Company of Jesus at Majorca was filled to the brim. These years had been occupied with fervent devotion and with hard and unremitting labors. He had borne constant interior trials, as well as infirmity of body. But throughout, he had remained the same devoted, loving, generous-souled lay brother.

He had seen those who were apparently much stronger than he laid to rest in the little Chapel of Our Lady, in the college church. But he had been spared from an early death, although several superiors had believed he would have gone, long before.

Now he was to witness the passing of a member of the community who had performed conspicuous work in the interests of Montesion. This was Father Juan Enconta who was greatly beloved by all his religious companions. It was often said of him that he had few equals in holiness and attainment.

As prefect of the Confraternity composed of students of the college, Father Enconta had so inspired his boys that they appeared more like novices than collegians. From their number he had chosen a select little group and formed them into what he called the *Academia,* a "school of the humble." He had trained them to follow the little way of humility by asking them to perform drudging duties, such as cleaning and dusting the classrooms and performing other lowly duties. Always at their head with the broom or mop, he had led these boys to real holiness.

The room assigned to Father Enconta, like that of Brother Alonso Rodriguez, was situated on the side of the house where the cold winds blew in season from the sea. But he had never considered his health. Now hard work, sacrifice, and denial of all bodily comfort had brought him to an early end.

Father Enconta was deeply devoted to the Blessed Virgin. As he lay dying, he cried out to her: "My Lady! For the services I have done you and induced others to do for you, I beg you to help me in this hour!"

Father Roca, the Provincial, was still visiting at Montesion when the death of this faithful follower of Ignatius Loyola took place, and he led the services for the departed. At their conclusion, the mortal remains of Father Enconta were laid beside those who had preceded him into eternity.

While Father Roca stayed at the College he lost no opportunity of conversing with Alonso. He inquired about the state of his health, whether his room was comfortable, and made other investigations in the interest of one whom he esteemed as a man of God.

To all this, Alonso had no answer but that he was very well off; all of the community were badly housed at this time, and the fact that he suffered from a catarrhal trouble, brought on by the dampness in his room, gave him no concern.

While a goodly portion of the new church had been erected, Father Coch, now vice-rector at Montesion, had done nothing to start the new college buildings, although they were badly needed. He had been about to start the work, when he, too, was called to his reward, after a life of hard work and good deeds for all.

July 22, 1587, saw the sorrowing community gathered about his bedside. It seemed incredible to them that Father Coch was about to leave them. He had been a kind and just superior, and an understanding friend. He had labored very hard to expand the property at Montesion under very trying and difficult circumstances. Even in the days of his early religious life, he had shown himself to be an organizer and executive, and the student body, whom he had then taught, had greatly loved him.

Now Father Coch lay stricken by a fatal illness. Yet he inspired all who visited his sick room by his patience and fortitude in suffering. Although his disease, dropsy, had induced a burning thirst, he refused to touch a drop of liquid of any kind unless his physician expressly ordered it.

At the bedside of the beloved Jesuit were the viceroy, Don Lewis Vich y Manrique, and his brother, the bishop of Majorca, and the community.

Father Coch had told his friends that he would die on the Feast of St. Mary Magdalen, July 22. This prediction was verified. On that day he rested from his life's labors, in the peaceful dignity of death.

Among those who had experienced singular kindnesses from Father Coch was Brother Alonso Rodriguez. While his friend and former superior was being anointed, Alonso had sought to enter his chamber. But so many others were there, kneeling in the narrow space about the bed, that he could not enter. So he had knelt outside, on the threshold, praying for the happy departure out of this world of his beloved friend.

As he knelt there, absorbed in prayer, he had a vision of the heavenly court, and a voice said to him, quite distinctly: "It is open for Father Coch." The voice also assured him that a like reception awaited him when his turn should come. It added, however, that he would be obliged to struggle on, for some years to come, on the hard path of obedience and mortification.

Brother Alonso Rodriguez did not speak to any except his superior of this interior illumination. But all believed, from seeing his radiant look, that he had received some assurance of Father Coch's reward. Otherwise, they knew that he would have been bent with sorrow, for he was very tenderhearted.

Father Coch had gone, but his memory lingered in Palma. For twelve years he had preached in that city and in other cities of Majorca. His power of reclaiming notorious sinners was very great, and his pulpit was always surrounded by a large congregation, including many nobles of the Island.

Alonso was aware of all this. But he believed that Father Coch had preached his best sermon as he lay submissively suffering in his last hours, declining, courteously, to receive any physical comforts in his strong trial. It had been Father Coch, more than any other, who was responsible for influencing the other superiors to leave Brother Rodriguez at Palma, and not return him to Spain, there to edify and assist the communities of other Jesuit foundations. Now no one would do what Father Coch had not wished should be done. Brother Alonso Rodriguez was safe, in the midst of those who revered and honored him.

The eighth of December, the Feast of the Immaculate Conception of the Holy Virgin, Mother of God, was always kept with solemn festivities in Palma. But this year it was to bring a catastrophe never before experienced in such intensity in the ancient city.

As the day advanced, the air became very sultry and the sky grew black. A high wind arose, gaining in ferocity until it burst into a tornado. It was accompanied by thunder storms of terrible violence, and the rain came down in sheets, turning the earth into a veritable sea.

One by one, or in groups, houses began to crash to the ground. For the most part, they were the flimsy dwellings of the poor. The large stone crosses which marked either side of the entrance to the city were blown down, and lightning struck the cathedral, breaking the beautiful rose window above the west door and scattering the splintered glass in all directions.

The College of Montesion was utterly unprepared for such a catastrophe. Shortly before the feast day, Father Hosta, who had recently been made rector, had begun to supervise the work of tearing down a part of the old walls. Therefore, that part of the college was fully exposed to the fury of the elements.

When the storm began to assume the aspects of a tornado, all the community at Montesion went to the chapel and joined in prayer, asking that the lives of all in the house and city might be spared. They mentioned, in particular, the persons living in the houses adjoining the college, nearest to the exposed walls.

However, the prayer was not answered in the way they hoped.

At the height of the storm, one of the exposed walls crashed down and outward. In its path were several small dwellings occupied by citizens of Palma.

These little houses went down under the falling masonry, which killed many under its terrible weight and injured many others.

The screams and moans of the dying and those less seriously injured were heart-rending.

The Jesuits had left the chapel as they heard the crash of

the falling walls and hurried out to help the victims of the tragic accident. They were passing among the men, women, and children, giving the last rites of the Church to some, and helping others as best they could.

Brother Alonso Rodriguez was sharing these heroic labors, when Father Hosta, his new rector, met him, and said to him:

"What are you doing here, Brother? Go at once to the sanctuary and pray God to stay this storm!"

At once Alonso left the scene and hurried into the chapel. With him went Brother Alonso Magi, who had some surgical skill, and who had helped tend the victims. Now he felt that he should go with Brother Rodriguez, in order to see that no mishap befell him.

Alonso knelt before the altar and began to recite three Hail Marys. Hardly had he finished the third, when the storm ceased and a light broke over the sky.

So sudden was the change that the community were able to enter the ruins, and, with the aid of torchlights, dig out those who were trapped under the mortar and timbers. Previously, because of the driving rain, it had been impossible to hold the torches.

While Father Hosta and his councilors were later discussing the marvel which had occurred, the object of their veneration was kneeling in his little cell, reciting the prayers he had assigned to himself, outside of the hour of meditation required by the rule.

He recited the Our Father and Hail Mary, each five times, in honor of the five wounds and of the sacred passion of Christ, asking through their merits that he might live as Christ lived and suffer as He suffered, being a close imitator of Him.

He then said the office of the Immaculate Conception, begging the most holy Virgin to obtain from her Son, by the sacred spotlessness in which she was conceived, that he might remain spotless as an angel, from sin, and so be pleasing to God.

After that he recited a Hail Mary and the Hail Holy Queen,

twelve times each, in honor of her purity, asking that all twenty-four hours of the day might find him free from all fault, through her blessed mediation.

Then Brother Alonso Rodriguez entered into the little company of his best-loved patron saints, and his guardian angel and other angels, entrusting to them his progress in virtue—St. Ildefonso, his name patron; St. Francis of Assisi, to whom he had been dedicated in baptism; St. Gabriel, St. Raphael, SS. Peter and Paul; St. John Baptist, St. James of Spain, St. Matthias, St. Joseph, and a few others.

When he had finished these prayers, Brother Alonso Rodriguez composed himself to rest on the hard planks he had placed over his mattress, laying himself down with the utmost reverence, in memory of the rude bed of the Cross on which the Saviour of the World had laid Him down.

IX

OFTEN the faithful thoughts of Brother Alonso Rodriguez turned lovingly to the yellow house in the Plaza del Azoquejo in Segovia, where the first four decades of his life had been passed. Again the tall straight figure of his mother moved through the now silent rooms, an infant clasped to her heart and several little ones tugging at her skirts. Again the blessed man, Father Peter Faber, crossed the threshold of the Rodriguez home in the Plaza, and sat in the great armchair, while he told of the beginnings of the Company of Jesus.

In the house where he had spent the few short years of his married life, again the slight form of a laughing girl-wife went to and fro, her dark eyes, veiled by long fringes, holding the light of a wondrous love for her husband and little children. The eyes of Spanish girls did not look deeply on life, and so they had little vision beyond those near and dear to them.

All these sacred memories were swiftly carried to the wounded feet of Christ by the man who had left the world and its comforts and attractions to serve as a lay brother in the Company of Jesus. Alonso Rodriguez was grateful for them, but he did not wish past joys revived.

From time to time, with the others of the Montesion community, he learned of great events and of illustrious personages who were following the standard of Father Ignatius Loyola. Names were beginning to be blazoned throughout the known world, names of brilliant theologians of the Company, who were successfully combatting the heresies of the day; names of others whose talents kept pace with their high virtues and achievements. And there were mere boys, of noble parentage and honored names, who had forsaken the treasures and emoluments of the world to put on the humble habit of the sons of the warrior-founder of Pamplona. Spiritual giants these were, running their course, as St. Paul said, and counting no pains too great to suffer if these helped them win their goal.

In 1568, the year of Alonso Rodriguez' entry into the College of Saint Paul at Valencia, a Polish boy, Stanislaus Kostka, a novice of the Company, had gone home to God on the feast day of Our Lady's Assumption. The fame of his holiness was now spreading everywhere, and it was believed that he would one day be elevated to the altars as a model for youth.

Brother Alonso Rodriguez cherished a strong devotion to the young Stanislaus, now enjoying the rewards of his sacrifices and labors in the eternal kingdom.

He was unaware that, at this very time, another illustrious youth, of Italian birth, was entering the Company at the Novitiate of Sant' Andrea, in the Eternal City. He was Luigi* Gonzaga. Already it was being noised about in the houses of the Society throughout Europe that Luigi Gonzaga was so distinguished for virtue that all felt he would be a worthy companion to the little Polish novice.

---

* Aloysius.

Brother Alonso Rodriguez was very happy when these reports were given out during recreation. He was more than ever conscious of the high dignity of his position as a member of the Company of Jesus, which had given and was giving heroes and saints to the Church and the world. He realized that all the great works and accomplishments which had stemmed from the Company since its foundation were due to the indomitable will and courage, the holy tenacity of purpose, and the extraordinary talents and spiritual gifts of his great Founder, Father General Ignatius Loyola.

Between the years 1540, when the Society was confirmed, and the death of Father General Ignatius in Rome, on July 30, 1556, the Founder had established twelve thoroughly organized provinces of the Society, and opened over one hundred houses, assigning the latter work to those of his sons best fitted for the task.

To the end of his gallant life, Father Ignatius Loyola had worked diligently and painstakingly on the Rules and Constitutions of his beloved Company. When he was elected first General, at the time of the visit of Father Peter Faber to Segovia, he continued his work of foundation, at the same time laboring to secure documents necessary for the lasting security of the organization.

On June 3, 1545, he obtained permission for all Jesuit priests to exercise all the functions of the priesthood; to preach, hear confessions, commute vows, and enjoy all the other offices and privileges granted to religious.

On June 5, 1546, Pope Paul III had granted permission for the admission of "coadjutors," both spiritual and temporal, to assist the priests of the Company in their various functions, according to their status. From this date, all the grades of the Company began to function, two preparatory and two final: 1. Professed of four vows. 2. Professed of three vows. 3. Spiritual Coadjutors. 4. Temporal Coadjutors.

Father Ignatius Loyola had won other privileges from Pope

Paul III. But always he had looked forward with eager anticipation to a very important Bull, which was eventually issued, by the successor of Pope Paul, Pope Julius III, on July 21, 1550.

This Bull presented the entire ideal and function of the Company of Jesus, but in more complete and precise formula than that issued by Pope Paul III. Father Ignatius had worked over this formula with Father Juan Polanco, his gifted secretary, from 1547 on. Gradually, he made alterations in the original document, clarifying and adding, always seeking the advice of those best versed in the subject matter involved.

When this Bull was issued by Pope Julius III, it became for all time the cornerstone of the Jesuit Institute.

Meanwhile, Father Ignatius was working on the Rules and Constitutions for his Company. He added an Examen, and the Rules of Modesty to these principal documents. In all, this marvelous man spent thirty-two years compiling his monumental works, at the same time gathering new companions about him, until his death, in 1556.

Brother Alonso Rodriguez pondered on the great history of the militant organization to which he was privileged to belong. He honored the departed veterans of Christ who had followed the standard of Christ through many vicissitudes, before attaining the eagerly sought crown. But he also honored the members of his own dear community at Montesion, who were working hard to fulfill the glorious motto of their Founder: "All for the greater glory of God."

The ranks of the living at the college had been sorrowfully depleted by a succession of deaths in the recent past. Now one more was to be added to the number.

Father Hosta, who had been made vice-rector upon Father Coch's death, was not to live to fill the new post entrusted to him. He had not been well since the death of his predecessor. Father Hosta had left Montesion to fill another important post, that of rector of the College of Barcelona. His fine ability and splendid character were recognized by the Father General, Claudius

Aquaviva. He did not live to assume his new duties, but died of malignant fever in February, 1588.

Brother Alonso Rodriguez had as his new rector Father Matthias Borrasa, who had conducted him from Valencia to Majorca during his novitiate. Father Borrasa was an organizer of great ability, and in June, 1588, he began the erection of a wing of the new College. This project was undertaken as the result of the report given to the General of the Company by the Father Visitor, who had taken note of the great need of improvements in the college property. The new college was to be a three-storied structure, standing at right angles to the church. It was to be connected with the temporary classrooms across the street by a wooden bridge.

Father Borrasa often asked the advice of Brother Alonso Rodriguez in regard to his labors. He soon remarked to the other Fathers that, while he often asked the Brother for some favor, Alonso had never asked him for any permission, except once, when he requested that he might be allowed to accompany one of the other Brothers to the country house, Santa Maria del Monte, since this Brother had asked for his company.

Father Borrasa knew quite well why the other Brother wanted Alonso to go with him. It was because he wanted to enjoy his holy and enlightened conversation, and, possibly, to disclose some of his problems to him.

The two Brothers had departed for Santa Maria. They enjoyed a pleasant visit. But when they returned, Alonso's companion told the rector that Brother Rodriguez had not looked at the beauty of the landscape all about him, nor had he been willing to allow himself a few grapes from the abundant vines to assuage his thirst, although the day was very warm.

The community at Montesion were soon called upon to engage in special devotions as the result of an outbreak of the plague at Barcelona. One of the Jesuits who succumbed to its effects was Father Juan Rico, a native of Valencia. Three Brothers also died in the same house. One was Brother Francis

Morey, who had been transferred from Palma to Barcelona. He was the deformed Brother, and he had spent twelve years with Brother Alonso Rodriguez at Montesion.

Alonso prayed fervently for the departed, including this zealous brother, who had been greatly attracted to Alonso from the time of his first meeting with him. Brother Morey was noted for his zeal for perfection and for his spirit of penance. While Alonso, in his discourses on the spiritual life, generally spoke of humiliations, as a means of reaching perfection, Brother Morey had spoken much of the love and bounty of God. Now these conversations would never be resumed.

Father Rico, who succeeded as rector at Montesion, in 1592, was a man of great mortification. Following the example set by other rectors of the College, he made it a point to consult Alonso before completing any important business transaction. Father Rico did not as yet know the power of Alonso's interior lights. An incident which took place soon after he became superior taught him a very useful lesson in this respect.

"I am going to preach in the church of the Convent of Mercede in this city, Brother," Father Rico said to Alonso. "I wish you to go with me. You may sit on the pulpit steps during my sermon."

The two Jesuits went to Mercede, and Father Rico began his sermon in the church, while Alonso sat, as he had been told to do, on the pulpit steps.

As he listened to his superior's discourse on the subject of forgiveness of one's enemies, he noted that, while Father Rico spoke earnestly and very brilliantly, the congregation did not seem to be greatly impressed by it.

As he was reciting the customary three Hail Marys, at the conclusion of the sermon, with the preacher and congregation, Alonso heard a voice, saying distinctly:

"The rector will atone for this sermon in Purgatory."

Alonso knew that the priest had employed the fashionable Castilian language in his delivery, rather than the popular

Majorcan, which all would have understood. For that reason, it was certain that many of the congregation, particularly the servants from the fine mansions, had not understood a word of it.

Alonso was gravely embarrassed by the interior communication. He could not make up his mind to tell Father Rico about it. But when he reached Montesion, he went to the Father Minister, and told him what had occurred. The Minister said to Alonso that, since he had received the warning message, he should convey it to Father Rico.

Alonso obeyed. When the rector heard what he had to say, he was greatly alarmed, as well as surprised. He thanked Alonso for the message, and said that he would never again preach in Castilian; that he knew he had committed a fault in doing so. He asked Alonso to write down some advice for him, and bring the paper to him.

In all simplicity, Alonso wrote down the counsel. He then brought the paper to his rector. Father Rico received it gratefully, and ever afterward treasured it as the work of one dear to God.

When he spoke of this incident to the Father Minister, Father Rico said:

"If the Rules of our Company should be lost, they would be preserved in the life of our saint."

In January, 1594, Father Matthias Reguer, a Catalan, was sent from Valencia to Palma to become confessor at Montesion.

Father Reguer had not previously met Brother Alonso Rodriguez, but he had heard much about him. He was hardly inside the house at Montesion when he looked for him, in order to speak to him about a certain difficulty he had experienced, a cause of great embarrassment to him.

He confided to Alonso that he suffered from an impediment in his speech, which became greatly aggravated when he was celebrating Mass. Although he could speak very well at other times, when he started to formulate the words of the Mass, they would not come correctly. He thought that the congregation must notice his difficulty, and the realization distracted him.

"Please pray for me, Brother," he said. "Pray that I may overcome this difficulty. I know your prayers will help me."

Alonso prayed. However, the prayers did not seem to be answered as he hoped, for Father Reguer was not cured of his trouble.

He prayed again. Then it was clear to him that he ought to ask the priest if he did not have some affectation of manner in his speech which was contrary to humility.

Father Reguer received the suggestion gladly. When Alonso had finished, he acknowledged, very humbly, that he had indulged in a certain affectation of that kind. He said that he was ready to humble himself before God in atonement for it, and stop doing it for the future.

The next time Father Reguer approached the altar to celebrate his Mass, he experienced no trouble in pronouncing the words of the holy Sacrifice.

As these and other favors granted through the prayers of the holy lay brother of Montesion became noised about in the other houses of the Aragon Province, and beyond, more requests came to Montesion, that Alonso might be sent to them, even if only for a short while. The requests were again denied.

All the community believed that they could absorb the aims of their holy rule and constitutions more readily by watching Brother Alonso Rodriguez than in any other manner. But Alonso himself believed that he was the poorest exemplar of them, although he prayed with ceaseless yearning to be able to comply with the pattern fashioned by Father Ignatius Loyola:

> Men crucified to the world, and to whom the world itself is crucified, such would the Rule of our life have us to be; new men, I say, who have put off their own affections to put on Christ; dead to themselves to live to justice; who with St. Paul in labors, in watchings, in fastings, in sweetness, in the Holy Ghost, in charity unfeigned, in the word of truth, show themselves ministers of God;

and by the armor of justice on the right hand and on the left, by honor and dishonor, by evil report and good report, by good success finally and ill success, press forward with great strides to their heavenly country, and by all means possible and with all zeal urge on others also, ever looking to God's greatest glory.

X

DURING the course of his religious life, Brother Alonso Rodriguez had always found it very difficult to fix his mind on any secular subject. Although his post as porter at Montesion brought many persons to the door, and he met citizens from all over Majorca, as well as from Palma itself, he had never learned to speak the Majorcan tongue. This was a dialect, quite different from the unadulterated Spanish of Castile. At most he could speak only a few words in the Majorcan, such as: "*Que voleu?*" – "What do you wish?" But he was always at his place at the appointed time, eager and prepared to perform his duties exactly as they were supposed to be performed.

The students of the College often met him as they came to consult their professors in the residence. Because he had grown more pale and worn as time went on, they found a new name for him: "Brother Death's Head." They were fully aware that they must be on hand for their classes on the minute, because Brother Alonso Rodriguez was never a minute late in ringing the bell, before and after class.

One of the rules of the Company of Jesus prohibited any of the religious of a house to speak to a member making his first probation in the postulancy without permission from the superiors. It happened that a young probationer named Garau, who occupied a separate room in the residence, became ill. He heard Alonso pass outside his door, and called to him.

There was no response. Alonso had heard the voice, but he had gone directly to find his superior, and ask permission to speak to the young man. When he received it, he hurried back to Garau, and gave him assistance. He first explained that he had not immediately answered the call because he had to ask permission to do so, otherwise he would have broken the rule.

The young man was much impressed by the spirit of the Brother, and from that time on revered him as a perfect religious.

Early in 1598 the group of lay brothers at Montesion was increased by the addition of two new members. They were Brother Bartolomé Roca and Brother Michael Serra.

The rector felt that he could do nothing better than to give these two Brothers into the care of Brother Alonso Rodriguez, in order that he might instruct them in their life and duties.

Brothers Roca and Serra were much pleased to find themselves in charge of the kindly, enlightened, and saintly Brother Rodriguez. Each day they spent some time listening to his exposition of the rule, and they marveled that a lay brother should know so much about the spiritual life in its most intimate phases.

Alonso told the two young men how to advance in the way of perfection more quickly, while performing the lowly duties of their state. He found that Brother Roca, in particular, absorbed his teaching with amazing facility. So Alonso taught him a sure way of advancing in virtue through meditation. He was to imagine that he had to construct an image of his crucified Saviour. He was to begin with the feet, follow with the hands, then the head, meanwhile studying the meaning of the wounds of our Lord imprinted upon them, and resolving to imitate the virtues He exemplified in His sacred passion.

Brother Michael Serra, Roca's companion in this study, did not find it easy to adapt himself to his new life. During the early part of his novitiate he suffered from mental depression, and he used to watch Alonso and wonder how this man, so bent and advanced in years, so frail and worn, could remain so cheerful always, and so ready to help others.

Brother Serra thought he would put the unalterable good humor and happy disposition of the older Brother to a test. Brother Serra had been given the office of Dispenser, and he had charge of the storeroom. His duty was to care for and distribute equally to all the community the necessary articles for their use; to see that the provisions were in good order and the place kept very clean. He also had charge of whatever food was left over after meals, and distributed it to the poor, as the Superior instructed him. As Dispenser, he also took care of the wine casks, and cleaned and prepared them to receive new wine when needed. He supervised the food provided for the sick and gave it out to the Infirmarian on request.

As Brother Serra was preparing some capers for the Community's evening meal on a certain occasion, Brother Rodriguez came into the storeroom and asked him to give some breakfast to the baker, who had just arrived at the college.

Brother Serra believed he had found the opportunity of testing Alonso, right then and there. He pretended to be very much annoyed by the request, and he said to Alonso: "Go away! Don't you see I'm busy? Why do you want to bother me?"

Brother Serra was a little frightened at his own temerity. But he was reassured when Alonso replied: "Dearest Brother, I did not order you to do it. I only wanted to let you know that the baker had come, so that you might give him his breakfast whenever it suited you."

The Brother Dispenser apologized to Alonso, not telling him what had really provoked the outburst. He never again doubted the great virtue of Brother Rodriguez, and he tried to help him in every possible way. He had many occasions of seeing the older Brother oppressed by many cares at his post as porter, as well as with infirmity and ill health. But he never observed that he grumbled or complained of his trials.

Alonso was charged with helping the Novice Master, who was entrusted with the formation of the lay brothers. His room was next to that of the probationers, and Brother Michael Serra used to listen in amazement to the sounds which came, somewhat muffled, from Alonso's cell. When the young Brother heard the dull swish of the discipline, he wondered if Brother Rodriguez might not hurt his health by such severe penance.

Brother Serra went to the Novice Master, Father Gabriel Bolicher, and asked him if he did not wish to stop Alonso from taking the discipline.

Father Gabriel told him: "No." He realized that God was leading this older Brother by hidden ways, and he had no wish to interfere.

Alonso often thought of the wonderful call to the foreign missions of the Company and regretted that he was unable to follow there, where other brave souls had gone before. As he sometimes stood in the patio of the college, beneath the whispering palms, he fancied that they were telling the story of the martyrs of the Company, who had won their palm at the hands of the benighted savages they had sought to convert. He continued to speak to the students about the noble apostolate to the foreign missions, which had so strongly attracted giant souls like Xavier, and which would continue to attract them unto the end of time.

Father de Villar, a member of the Montesion community, had just received into the Company a student named Diego de Moranta. This young man's father was a member of the Royal Council of Majorca. Diego had often talked with Brother Alonso Rodriguez, and brought his spiritual problems to him for counsel and solution.

Alonso had spoken earnestly to Diego of the vocation of the foreign missions. He had taught him the first elements of spirituality, and watched him grow in the way of perfection with ever increasing joy.

Diego responded to the training by asking to be sent to the dangerous but much-coveted post.

His plea received the favorable consideration of the superiors, and a short time later he went to the scene of his selfless labors for souls, to win the crown sought by every apostle — martyrdom.

A short time after Diego had left Majorca, his brother, Antony, asked to be admitted to the Society. The Father Visitor, Father Laurence San Juan, who was then at Montesion, granted the request. Antony followed his brother, when the time had come, and in far-distant Paraguay worked with great fruits for the christianization of the natives of that country.

Spain, since her christianization, had always been intensely devoted to the Blessed Virgin. In the kingdom of Aragon, as elsewhere, her glorious virtues and prerogatives were commemorated with great pomp and splendor. Majorca shared in the honors and festivities. During the octave of her assumption, in particular, the college of Montesion held fiesta in her honor. Each year, on this great feast, Brother Alonso Rodriguez had received some distinguished favor from his Lady and Queen. This year her bounty was to surpass all previous favors.

During the eight days of the octave, a lovely statue of the Virgin Mother was laid out, in a splendid catafalque, in each of the churches of Palma. The people kept watch in turns at her bier, and on the feast day itself, the ceremonies of her interment were carried out.

At the cathedral in Palma, all the dignitaries of Church and State attended the ceremonies. Thousands of persons from other cities and towns of the Island came to the city to participate in the solemn rites.

Brother Alonso Rodriguez, with the other members of the Montesion community, had attended the various services during the day. Now evening had come, and he sat in his little room, looking out on the courtyard of the church, meditating on the glories of the Queen of Heaven, his beloved patroness and guide.

The city was quiet at last, for the visitors had departed for other parts, and the townspeople were at the cathedral, assisting at the solemn procession in which the statue of the holy Virgin was carried to its tomb in a side chapel.

As he meditated and prayed, Brother Rodriguez felt that he

was slipping away from the little room. He saw before him a procession far more glorious than that being held in the town at that hour. In it, the Blessed Virgin walked, attended by angels to the gates of heaven. There other angels received her and conducted her to the throne of her Son. Then the lovely Queen entered into her great triumph, while celestial harmony sounded through the heavenly courts.

This inner vision lasted for many minutes. When Brother Rodriguez finally lost it, there was only the little room, with its four walls and its simple furnishings, before him.

As the rule required, he gave a faithful account of this vision to his confessor, who was convinced that a great grace had been granted to the humble Brother, who had already told him of other similar favors he had received. The confessor was certain that the house at Montesion harbored one of God's chosen souls.

Alonso always rose early in the morning, even in the coldest weather of the winter. He was the first to appear at the chapel door. On three days of the week he received Holy Communion at the first Mass. The happiness which radiated from his thin face as he returned to his place from the altar rail was such that his brother religious always made it a point to watch him at that moment.

Brother Bartolomé Roca had been made Infirmarian soon after coming to Palma, because he knew a little about medicine and the care of the sick. He was very anxious about Alonso's health. Because he was afraid his beloved friend might become gravely ill as a result of his zeal and penance, he told the superior that he thought Brother Rodriguez should be restrained in his devotion.

Father Matthias Borrasa was now rector. He told Brother Roca to send Alonso to him.

When Alonso came, Father Borrasa said to him: "Brother, it is my wish that for the present you rise early for Holy Communion only on Sundays and holydays. You have been overdoing for a long time. We don't want to lose you. You know, we have already lost several of our Fathers and Brothers."

Alonso bowed to the obedience, although he felt it keenly. He thanked the rector for his interest, and bowing low, left his presence. When he met Brother Roca, he did not charge him with having told the rector about him, although he was sure the Infirmarian had done so.

Sometimes Brother Roca, whose duties were very taxing at times, scolded Alonso a little for his want of care of himself. Once, when he heard Alonso cry out: "Jesus!" and he knew he was in great pain, he went to him and chided him for having made himself ill. Alonso thanked Bartolomé for the scolding.

Brother Roca naïvely confided to Father Borrasa that he had tried very hard to make Brother Rodriguez slip just a little, but that he had never been able to do so.

The spiritual sons of Father Ignatius Loyola at Montesion attracted many penitents from all over Palma to their confessionals, although there were numerous other churches in the city. Occasionally, some incident occurred to bring Brother Rodriguez into close communication with certain of these persons, and to illustrate his power with God still more brightly.

A penitent of one of the Fathers, a citizen of Palma named Cristopher Colomer, was taken very ill. He suffered from a burning fever, and his doctors had denied him all liquid refreshment because of the nature of his disease. Cristopher had received the Holy Viaticum from Father Gabriel Montener, his parish priest. But when no one was at hand to stop him, he got up from his bed, dressed himself, and made his way, in great misery, to Montesion.

At the Porteria he found his friend, Brother Alonso Rodriguez. He begged Alonso to give him a little drink of water, to relieve the dryness of his mouth and throat.

Alonso led the man to his room. He told him to kneel down at the foot of a large wooden crucifix which stood near the bed.

Cristopher did so. Then Alonso knelt down beside him.

"Say the Hail Mary, five times," he told Cristopher.

The man answered that he could not make the effort—that he was too weak.

But Alonso insisted that he try. He did so, and found that he was able to finish the prayers.

Alonso then blessed some water in a glass, and handed it to Cristopher, who drank it all.

Then he rose, and was astonished and overjoyed to find that he felt normal. But he was a little drowsy, and Alonso told him to lie down on the bed for a while.

Cristopher lay down on the hard mattress which served as Alonso's bed. He fell asleep and slept for about fifteen minutes. When he awoke, he found Alonso still praying beside him.

"Brother Rodriguez," Cristopher said, "are there any pumpkins cooking in the kitchen? I seem to smell some."

Alonso went off to find out. He discovered that no pumpkins were on the fire, and he knew that Cristopher was so hungry that he had imagined he detected the odor.

The rejoicing Cristopher left for his home. When he reached there, his family was in consternation over his absence. As they saw him enter the house, in apparent health, they were amazed, but deeply thankful.

A little later, Cristopher returned to thank Alonso for curing him. He knelt at the Brother's feet and kissed his habit before Alonso could stop him from doing so. Alonso, greatly distressed at this homage, bade him rise and think no more about what he had been able to do for him.

His Holiness Pope Clement VIII had fixed the term of all Jesuit provincials and rectors as three years at one time. Later, this legislation was abrogated. Now it was in force, and it caused a frequent change in the rectorship of Montesion, as in other houses of the Company.

On May 3, 1600, Father Borrasa's term at Montesion ended, and he retired from his post. Father Bolicher remained in the college as vice rector. In July, Father Melchior de Valpedrosa succeeded Father Juste as provincial, and Father Juan Rico became Visitor of Montesion.

Father Rico had previously served the college as its rector, so that he was thoroughly familiar with it. After he had fulfilled his duties as Visitor, he was given his old charge of rector at Montesion.

An able organizer, the new rector put his shoulder to the task of promoting the interests of the college in a very important way. He formed a class in Moral Theology and engaged Doctor Juan Forteza, a doctor of the law, and member of an influential family in Majorca, as first professor of the new faculty.

Father Rico, like Brother Alonso Rodriguez, had formerly been a married man, and had also entered the Company after the death of his wife. He went to work to push forward the completion of the new college church. On Candlemas Day, 1601, the high-vaulted artistic sanctuary was so nearly finished that Monsignor Vich y Manrique celebrated the first Mass on its altar.

The bustle occasioned by the building had not interrupted the serene busy community life. The days passed swiftly, and June came around, to bring a real cross to Montesion.

Brother Diego Ruiz, the cook, who had entered the Society the year before Alonso, and who had been his first companion and associate at Palma, taking his first vows with Alonso, passed from earth to his reward.

Alonso prayed long and fervently for his soul. At the moment of Brother Ruiz's death he began the recitation of the three rosaries ordered to be said for all departed at this time. He had finished two of them and was beginning the third, when, in his favored little room, the gracious Lady, who had before appeared to him, stood close by. He looked up into her face, to learn whether she wished him to continue the prayers.

But the Lady said to him: "There is no need, for Diego is in my company."

Alonso came back to earth with a sense of overwhelming comfort and peace. He hastened to tell his superiors about the vision, and they rejoiced with him.

As God called one after another precious soul from the community he sent others to fill their places and carry on their interrupted work. Now the Brothers rejoiced to welcome into their midst Antony Mora, twenty-one years old, a lay brother postulant.

Antony was a Majorcan, and he had heard a great deal about Brother Alonso Rodriguez. He was immediately attracted to him when they met, and he carefully noted the virtues and characteristics of the older Brother. He saw that Alonso made frequent visits to the Blessed Sacrament, and he found that he was to be privileged to share, with the other Brothers, the reading and counsel given for an hour each day to their group by the saintly Brother.

Antony found that when Alonso proposed the points of meditation, he made them so clear and simple that he seemed to show his disciples the personages and scenes of which he spoke. If they sometimes accompanied him outside, into the streets, they noticed that he always chose any rough place there might be in the path, for his walk. They noted how cheerfully he kept the rule, and they were anxious to follow his beautiful example.

Brother Antony Mora was a lively young brother, who reminded his superiors of the irrepressible Ribadeneira, Father Ignatius Loyola's companion in the early days of the Company. Antony took great pains to pick little nosegays of blossoms to place in Brother Rodriguez' room when his friend and mentor was not feeling well, because Ignatius had said that such little objects should be placed in sick rooms, to divert the religious who were ill. Antony did not think Alonso ever looked at them, however.

This young Brother was distressed to find that Alonso waited on him during his postulancy as if he were his servant. While Antony was in his room, following the Spiritual Exercises, Alonso, whose room was close by, often retired to his, and from the sounds heard through the walls, the Brother postulant knew that he was taking a severe discipline.

Rumors of significant events in the Company happening elsewhere penetrated to Majorca, and reminded the community at Montesion that, as the sovereign Pontiff had exclaimed, upon examining the work of Father Ignatius Loyola: "The finger of God is here!"

Some few years before this time, on June 21, 1591, the young Italian scholastic, Luigi Gonzaga, had died in the Eternal City. So the community at Montesion were thrilled to learn at this time of the apparition of the holy scholastic to a cloistered nun named Mary Magdalen de Pazzi, in Italy. This, and a miracle which followed, indubitably through the intercession of the young Jesuit noble, had caused his cult to spread rapidly throughout northern Italy and Rome. It was prophesied that some day public veneration would be permitted him.

In his selfless heart, Brother Alonso Rodriguez rejoiced over this new development in favor of a spiritual son of Father Ignatius Loyola, whose own beatification seemed imminent. But Brother Rodriguez thought that, while others were bringing glory to the Company, he alone was crawling along like a snail, whereas the Founder had bade his sons: "Go, and kindle a fire upon the earth!"

Sometimes, particularly on the great liturgical feasts of the Church, the rector of Montesion asked Brother Alonso to preach in the refectory at meal times.

Alonso willingly did this, believing that it afforded him a good opportunity of suffering humiliation. He was never allowed more than half an hour for his preparation, sometimes less. The superiors were apt to call on him at some unexpected moment. He did not realize that they believed the Holy Spirit enlightened him in a very special way, so that he did not really need to prepare.

The discourses which he gave at these times inspired and encouraged to perseverance all who heard them. One of the lay brothers, Brother Jose Rahohú, began to promote the veneration of his holy associate, privately, because he thought that every Brother in the house would profit by it.

One evening it happened that, although dinner was finished and the remains of the last course had been removed while Alonso was preaching, the Superior did not tell him to stop, as usual. So he continued, while all at table sat spellbound at the eloquence of wisdom issuing from the lips of a lay brother. Alonso was speaking of the presence of God, and of how sweet and tender He was to those who loved and served Him. His usually pallid face was flushed by the strength of his emotions, and his voice trembled as he went on.

Finally, the rector gave the signal for the end of the discourse. Before Alonso left the refectory, he called him and told him to write out what he had said, as far as he could recall it, and give him the paper. The discourse which had so impressed the community was entitled: "God's Love to Man." It was arranged in classic form, as were all Spanish sermons in that day. There was the text, introduction, Ave Maria, proofs, conclusion, and peroration. Alonso sometimes rambled a little, because of his advancing age and his weakness of body. But what he said came from his heart and soul, and those who heard it realized that the speaker was truly a man of God.

Brother Bartolomé Roca, one of the newer members of the lay brothers' group, continued to find great help in the counsels of this wise teacher. He always said that it was Brother Rodriguez' example that had led him to join the Company, and others said the same. Brother Rodriguez frequently told them that the life of a lay brother in the Company of Jesus was a blessedly secure and fruitful one. Free from the awful responsibilities of the priesthood, with its cares and burdens, the lay brothers enjoyed all the other privileges granted to religious. Their life of manual labor or of other lowly duties about the houses of the Society left their minds free from secular pursuits, for they did not have to engage in serious study of the arts and sciences, or teach in the colleges. They could live the life of contemplation freely and lovingly while performing their ordinary routine tasks. And so it should be very easy for them to reach a state of union with God. . . . Alonso spoke in such winning manner of this vocation that the Brothers in the house realized all the more the truth of his words.

As he learned more about the life of the blessed young Neopolitan scholastic, Luigi Gonzaga, Alonso was much pleased to find that, while in the novitiate, Luigi had shown a preference for the company of the lay brothers, and had begged to be allowed to go with them to visit the hospitals and prisons. He was given permission, and, to his great joy, to go out in a threadbare coat, which was much too short for him.

Alonso believed that this elect soul would win many vocations to the Company. The students at Montesion, gathered about Brother Rodriguez, to hear him tell the story of Luigi's life, were much impressed by it.

The exhumation of the scholastic's body had recently taken place, revealing that the bones were intact, each in its proper position, with the head slightly inclined, as Luigi had carried it in life. It was said that Father General Claudius Aquaviva intended to have these sacred bones moved to a more fitting resting place, since the veneration of Luigi was increasing from day to day.

The life of the religious at Montesion had gone on in peace and quiet for some time. They had believed that the troubles stirred up in the past by Algerian corsairs were at an end. But now these pirates again made their presence felt, as they worked all along the shores of the Mediterranean Sea. So disastrous were their incursions on mercantile shipping in that area that the Spanish officials were obliged to adopt stern measures for their destruction.

A fleet of seventy-three large galleys was assembled, with strong forces on board, for the purpose of taking Algiers. The fleet had sailed into the Bay of Palma, with many royal officials and officers on board. But the time was inopportune for such a gathering, because an intense heat wave swept over that part of the world just then. The crowded condition of the vessels, added to the torrid weather, brought on a plague, and great numbers of the officers and crews had to be taken ashore and carried to the general hospital at Majorca.

The Jesuit community at Montesion went immediately to the aid of the victims. Four fathers traveled through the city, seeking alms for the stricken persons, in the form of food and clothing. They also served as nurses for the sick.

Although he was at this time seventy years old, Brother Alonso Rodriguez took his turn in performing various works of mercy. The thought of possible contagion did not trouble him, nor did the weakened state of his body. He went among the poor sufferers, aiding and consoling them, and preparing a number for a good death.

Some of the citizens of means in Palma, who recognized the great virtues of Alonso, gave him alms from time to time, for the purchase of necessaries for the sick. His superiors, having full confidence in his good sense and business acumen, did not interfere in any way with his activities, but allowed them full scope.

The community noticed that, while practically everyone else in Palma went to see the magnificent fleet in the bay, Brother Rodriguez remained behind. They were well aware that, even if he did not wish to visit the quay for the purpose, he could have seen it from the azeota, or veranda, of the college. But he did not go there to inspect it. It eventually sailed out of the bay, leaving the victims of the plague behind.

Fate was not kind to the gallant expedition. Before long, news came that it had been driven by a furious storm on the coasts of Africa, where it met heavy losses and only escaped complete destruction by turning back and sailing for Spain. One section arrived in the harbor of Barcelona, the other, consisting of forty-six galleys, went on to Palma.

The troops were sadly weakened by hunger and the hazards they had undergone. Many on board had now contracted the dread plague, and all were miserable and unhappy.

Again the Montesion Fathers and Brothers went to the rescue of the new victims of these misadventures, and worked without ceasing to help them.

Such a sustained siege of strenuous work as well as exposure to contagion was too much for the strength of some of the religious. Two Fathers, Father Barcelo and Father Bernard Crespin, died victims of their charity.

After Father Crespin's funeral, Alonso made known a pact he had shared with him: "Each week I am to say a rosary for Father Crespin, and he has to say a Mass for me. If he dies before me, all my life, I am to say one rosary each week for him, also fifty additional rosaries. He has to say a Mass for me each month. And if I die before him, he has to say twenty rosaries for me, and each month one Mass for the whole of his life."

Alonso knew that his part of the pact was now to be fulfilled. For Father Crespin had died before him. While he faithfully remembered the priest's soul before God, he believed that he had a new intercessor before the eternal throne.

The royal fleet had left Palma, to go to Barcelona. The Father Provincial and a companion Jesuit were on board. But the corsairs, made bold by the failure of the Spanish fleet at Algiers, had renewed the depradations. They had captured a Majorcan merchantman on its way from Barcelona to Palma, and had made the crew and passengers captives. Among the latter was a Jesuit lay brother who had been assigned by his superiors to the college at Montesion.

The Provincial, leaving Palma, had taken Father Juan Rico with him, thinking that Father Rico's health would benefit by the change. Father Borrasa remained at Montesion as vice rector. Father Borrasa saw that Brother Rodriguez had become enfeebled by his work among the sick, and he told him to take a little walk in the country, to breathe in some fresh air and enjoy the loveliness of the landscape. Another lay brother was sent with him.

The two religious left the college by the Puerta del Campo and entered the green meadows in a spot close to a little eminence. From this spot they could enjoy a glorious view of the bay, headlands, and mountains. Because the verdure was so lush in the place, it was called Salvaverde, Green Hill.

Invited by his companion to look out over the bay, Alonso did so. It seemed to him that it was the blue mantle of his beloved Queen and Mother, spread out in folds, and sprinkled with millions of foam blossoms, like pearls. Here and there the mantle was tucked in at some little cove, where the tall palms reflected their proud trunks and foliage in the silver-blue mirror beneath.

As he looked, to please his companion, Alonso had been speaking. But now he stopped, and gazed more fixedly, straight out on the water.

He seemed to see there a great armada. Christ, our Lord, was on board, in the van, with our Lady. The fleet was manned by angels.

He did not mention the vision to the other brother, but waited until he met Father Borrasa later. Then he told him what should be done, according to the message revealed in this vision.

The king was to go in person at the head of a vast army, and drive back and conquer the Moors. The country of those infidels would then be converted to Christianity, without further trouble.

Father Borrasa thanked Alonso, and told him to continue praying that the promise would soon come true.

At the time of Father Bernard Crespin's death, his young nephew was enrolled as a student in the College of Montesion. The boy had entertained no thought of becoming a Jesuit, until Alonso had foretold his vocation. This happened as the young man was passing through the Porteria, with some other boys.

Jerome was the last to pass, and when he did so, Alonso stretched out his hand above his head and told him: "You are to enter the Company in place of your uncle." The boy had laughed at this, because he was one of the youngest students in the college. However, some time later, when he had become old enough, he asked to be admitted into the novitiate. As he waited in the Porteria for the vice-rector to come down and meet him, he was reading a book by a priest-author, entitled: *On The Excellence Of The Religious Life.*

He did not hear Brother Alonso Rodriguez come up behind him. But he heard his voice, saying: "Don't you realize, sir, that you are planning a higher state than that of your brothers?"

Jerome wondered how the venerable Brother knew of his intention, since he had not mentioned it to anyone.

During the thirty years he had spent in the Company of Jesus up to this time, Alonso had borne gladly the fatigues and burdens which his frail health and his advanced age imposed. Added to these, his long vigils in prayer, and his stern penances had not ceased, from the beginning of his novitiate. He had lost most of his teeth, but this fact did not trouble his peace of mind. He told the community that what he lacked in teeth, God had made up to him in his fingers, because with them he could crush the hard portions of his bread. When others tried to do this for him, he courteously declined the aid, explaining, again, that his fingers were excellent servants, and would serve him.

A young scholastic asked Alonso if it was necessary to sweep out his room three times each week, since Father Ignatius had prescribed that it should be done "at least every third day." The Society understood this to mean that twice each week was sufficient. But Alonso replied to the scholastic's question:

"My dear Brother, I sweep mine out four times each week, because the Rule orders it to be done at least three times. Now, that expression, 'at least' seems to me to require more, and so I sweep the room four times. That is safer."

When another scholastic questioned him on his idea of obedience, Alonso replied:

"If the Superior were to forbid me, when I have the keys of the gate, to open to anyone, and the king was in the city and wished to enter; and if his bodyguard was at the door, bidding me to open to him, what should I do? I should beg his majesty to pardon me because I was not able to admit him; for obedience had ordered me not to open the gates to anyone. It would seem that I certainly would neither open for the king nor for any of his suite, even though I should be ill-treated and badly used by them.

"It appears to me that in like circumstances, and in all others which might occur, no matter what threats should be used, I would never let myself be troubled as long as I kept my heart solidly rooted in God by the orders of the superior. I know there is nothing so firm as the heart which is under the shelter of obedience. Then, I am sure, too, that it is the command of God, and that I am as ready to do it without hesitation, as Abraham when he was bidden to sacrifice his son, Isaac. So, all the ills of this life would not suffice to cause me to fail in obedience, for I do not doubt that, as I take in hand the cause of God by obeying Him, this same Lord would have such a care of His obedient servant that all would turn out to the glory of God."

Brother Alonso Rodriguez was quite correct in his interpretation of the rule of obedience. But it happened that soon this literal view proved very troublesome to some distinguished personages.

The Course of Philosophy was solemnly opened at Montesion College on September 10, 1603. The occasion was also marked by the presentation of an allegorical drama, which was a type of entertainment very popular at that time. The drama scheduled to be presented at Montesion was: *The Triumph Of Virtue.* A noted professor of the drama had recently come over from Spain to coach the cast.

The bishop of Majorca, Juan Vigo y Manrique, and his brother, the viceroy, with the magistrates of Palma, and others of note had been invited to attend the presentation. In order that the place might not be overcrowded by the ordinary citizens and no room left for the guests of honor, the Father Rector had given orders that no one was to be admitted to the college before a certain hour.

The viceregal party, however, arrived on the premises very early, and quite unexpectedly. The bodyguard knocked briskly at the gate of the college, announcing the arrival of the bishop and viceroy, and the others of their group.

No one answered the knock. It was repeated, but still no response was forthcoming. The bodyguard pounded loudly and continued doing so until the rector, who had been told what was going on, hurried to the door and admitted the party. He apologized profusely for the inconvenience caused to his illustrious guests, and explained that he had told the Brother Porter not to open the gate until a certain time.

The rector believed that the time had come to relieve Brother Rodriguez of his charge. For, while such obedience was laudable, it might occasion further embarrassment in the future, and those who were not religious would, perhaps, not so highly value that type of service.

Alonso was quite ready to do whatever he was told. Because of his advanced years, he was relieved from active duty in the house. Yet, often, the Father Rector discovered him wielding a big broom with great difficulty, and carrying on stanchly as he tried to make himself useful to his superiors.

No one was disposed to censure Brother Rodriguez because he did not conform to the ideas which others held in certain matters.

Even the minor canon of the Cathedral, Don Pasquale, was pleased, rather than displeased when, after he had approached Alonso in the church and said he would like to have a chat with him, the faithful Brother replied, meekly:

"We ought not to talk in God's presence, even about holy subjects, because the church is a place for prayer only."

The canon was not only a common-sense, but a humble man. He returned home, feeling that he had received a much-needed lesson in courtesy to his divine Lord.

XI

IN FEBRUARY, 1604, Father Gabriel Alvarez, who had served for some time as companion to the Provincial of the Jesuits at Majorca, became rector at Montesion. When he was about to enter upon his new duties, the Provincial, Father Diego Escriva, charged him as an obligation to make a most minute examination of the life of Brother Alonso Rodriguez. The Provincial stated that the extraordinary, and in some instances seemingly miraculous nature of his acts was such that the Company could not assume the responsibility of allowing this brother to continue his present mode of life if he was found to be the victim of delusion.

"Do this promptly and thoroughly, Father," the Provincial said to Father Alvarez. "Gather all the writings of Brother Rodriguez; obtain written testimonials from him, and then bring them to me."

Father Alvarez felt this order to be very distasteful and against his inclination. But he followed it without delay. He requested Alonso to furnish him with a complete record of his experiences in religious life, particularly in relation to anything out of the ordinary and of an apparently supernatural nature.

Alonso at once started to compile the record Father Alvarez desired. The task was a little difficult, because much had occurred in the long years of his life in the Company, and the record must necessarily be full. His style of writing was involved, and his natural modesty shrank from exposing his interior to such a comprehensive scrutiny. Yet he worked hard at his task, and when he had finished it to the best of his ability, and had carefully revised it, he carried the manuscript to Father Alvarez.

The rector considered that this data was of a confidential nature, and so revealed it to no one in the house. He read the composition from beginning to end, attentively and also reverentially, and when he had finished, he was filled with a sense of his own unworthiness and of the exalted virtue of the simple lay brother. He sent the paper to the Provincial, as he had been instructed to do, and left the matter to his judgment.

Meanwhile, Alonso continued in his way of humility and penance with a serene countenance and obedient heart.

The community continued to test him, now and then, in order to find out how far he would go in certain matters.

One winter evening, shortly after Alonso had begun to write his memoirs for the Provincial, with the scholastics he was spending the recreation period in the room of Father Gonzalez, a member of the community.

Father Gonzalez had been speaking of the immense labors and sacrifices which were the lot of the Jesuit missionaries in the distant Indies, and of the great work waiting to be done for God in those parts.

Alonso listened with rapt attention to what the priest was saying. When Father Gonzalez had finished, he remarked:

"Father, I am nobody and good for nothing. But I think, if it were well, and obedience should send me there without my asking, I should be very happy to go, because I would believe it was God who ordered it."

Father Gonzalez thought he would try an experiment, to see what Alonso would do if he were actually ordered to the Indies. He knew that at this very time the Provincial was delving into the Brother's life and acts, and this seemed to be an opportune moment to make a little test of his own.

"Well, Brother," he said to Alonso, "since you feel that way about it, go to the Indies. I order you to go."

The scholastics opened their eyes very wide when they heard the command. Like Father Gonzalez, they waited in some trepidation to see what would happen.

It was then after nine o'clock in the evening. A chill wind rustled through the palm trees just outside the window of the room. The night was cold and dark, and Alonso was an elderly man, and very infirm. Father Gonzalez spoke aside to one of the young Jesuits, and the scholastic at once left the room.

Alonso rose, bowed low, and went out, clad only in his habit and cap. As he approached the college door, he asked the Brother Porter, who had replaced him in that duty, to let him out.

The Porter had been told by the scholastic, whom Father Gonzalez had sent to him, what to expect. He asked Alonso:

"What do you want, Brother?"

"I want you to open the door, for I am off for the Indies," was the answer.

The Brother Porter was a little amused at the naïve request. He had orders from the Father not to open the door, so he replied:

"What! Without coat or hat, you want to go out at this hour?"

Alonso answered: "Yes. Since obedience sends me off at this hour, it is the right time to go."

"Have you got your letter of obedience?" the Brother Porter inquired next. "You know, you cannot start off on a journey, nor can I let you pass without it. If you have not got it, go for it, and when you return with it, I will let you out."

Alonso went to find the rector, Father Alvarez. But Father Alvarez had been told by Father Gonzalez that, without doubt, Alonso would come to him for the letter. The rector said, with studied coldness, after listening to the request:

"Well! Well! Here you are nothing but a bother to everyone, and you want to go to the Indies!"

Alonso smiled and thanked the rector for the rebuke.

"Think no more of it," continued Father Alvarez, and he dismissed Alonso.

Afterward, Father Alvarez told Brother Mora that when someone had asked Alonso how far he would have gone on the way to the Indies, had he been allowed to go, he had said: "I would have continued until the water came up to my face. I would think I should return then, having satisfied obedience."

During the more than twenty years he had held the office of Porter, Alonso had suffered much because of his strict adherence to his ideal of obedience. A few of the Fathers were not entirely charitable in their appraisal of his motives. In his later life Alonso confessed that sometimes he had felt a strong impulse to argue the point with some of the theologians at Montesion, who held different views from his own.

The rector asked him to write down his concept of the obedience of a Jesuit, and he did so. When Father Alvarez read what he had written, he felt that he had received a powerful instruction. For Alonso had set down his ideas as follows:

The first degree is to believe by faith that whatever a superior orders is the command of God, and so carry it out blindly; and this not by sight, but simply by faith, which is to believe what you do not see.

The second is: God communicated to me a light from above, which showed me that obedience proceeds from Him, so that I do not notice the man, but only God, from Whom the order comes.

The third degree: I recognize that it is not the voice of my superior which orders me, but the voice of God Himself.

The fourth degree is that God bestows as a reward for the practice of the three foregoing degrees so powerful a light about obedience that I see clearly, in the presence of God, without any exercise of my reasoning faculties, that obedience is the voice of God, just as the angels do in the Lord Himself. For God reveals Himself to me, though with less light than to the angels, who see Him face to face.

One of those who could best attest to the mortification and penance practiced by Brother Rodriguez was the Father Minister at Montesion. One night, in particular, as he was making the rounds of the rooms to make certain that all were in bed, coming to Brother Rodriguez' room, he found its occupant, although at the time he had a cold, lying on the boards of the bed, with no mattress in evidence, and only the sheet and coverlet protecting him.

"Brother!" expostulated the Minister. "How can you lie there in that state?"

The Minister did not receive any information from Alonso as to the whereabouts of the missing mattress, for Alonso did not know where it was. As the priest was standing in the room in wonderment, trying to think where it could be, Alonso told him: "I am perfectly all right, Father! Glory be to God! It does not matter, at all. I am quite well off as I am."

The Minister went off to tell the rector that Brother Rodriguez' mattress had vanished, as if carried away by angels.

The rector summoned Brother Serra, then acting as Infirmarian part of the time. Brother Serra had charge of Alonso. Father Alvarez instructed him to go to Brother Rodriguez, tell him to rise at once, and have the mattress replaced on the bed.

The mystery of the missing mattress was soon solved by the Infirmarian. Another Brother had carried it away, to lay it temporarily on the couch which the new bishop of Majorca Don Lasso Sedeno, had occupied during a siesta hour. The bishop was greatly devoted to the Jesuits and he had paid a visit to Montesion immediately after coming to Palma. The mattress had served him for his rest period, but it had not been replaced.

Whether or not his uncomfortable position in bed without the mattress had brought on an indisposition, Alonso contracted a cold soon after this. Father Alvarez thought he knew something of medicine, but, unfortunately, he overestimated his powers. He asked the house physician to give Alonso a certain medicine, which was done, but it only aggravated his illness.

Alonso did not complain of his distress, but continued to take the medicine when it was given to him. Brother Serra saw, in alarm, that it was not the right prescription for Alonso's condition. But, just as he was about to tell the rector about it, the patient became much better. Brother Serra thought that God wanted His friend better, despite the potion he had taken repeatedly, although it was not the right remedy for his trouble. However, the Brother Infirmarian made up his mind that if he himself should fall ill, he would be very watchful to see that the rector did not prescribe for him.

As had happened in Alonso's experience as a wool merchant in Segovia, a serious economic depression had settled over Majorca. Agriculture was at a low ebb, partly due to the severe droughts common to the island. But the main reason was the monopoly by a few rich families of the great properties. Unemployment was increasing, and with it a crime wave that extended in all directions.

On their arrival in Majorca to make a foundation the Jesuits had witnessed the effects of these evils. But their zeal for the well-being of the people had somewhat tempered the strain and bettered conditions. In the country places, however, the banditry were not so easily accessible to the Fathers. The bandits had taken to the adjacent hills and from there descended at intervals on the near-by cities and villages. Armed violence and even bloodshed had resulted.

It often happened in Spain and her possessions that two distinguished families carried on a perennial feud, as in Italy. In Majorca, the Puigdorfilas and the Torrelos had divided the population into two factions. Even in religious interests they would not come together. Father Bartolomé Coch, the deceased rector of Montesion, had halted the feud, in large part, by his constant efforts for peace. Now trouble was brewing stronger than ever, and the Fathers were gravely concerned over the situation.

The town of Soller, which Brother Alonso Rodriguez had visited with the late Father Juan Aguirre, was seething with disorders. While it was one of the most prosperous districts of Majorca, because of its flourishing olive groves, the citizens felt very insecure inside or outside the walls which had been built around the parish church as a bulwark against the Moors.

The Pass, the sole road leading from Soller to Palma, was in the keeping of bandoleros, outlaws of the worst caliber. The viceroy had very few troops to send against them, and he could not supply the needed reinforcements to the magistrates of Soller, who did not dare to appear in the streets unless escorted by a band of horsemen and musketeers.

All the houses of the town were heavily barricaded at sunset each day, and guards placed before the doors. A number of the townspeople had been wounded by the clubs of the outlaws, others killed in the strife.

The viceroy had come to the end of his powers in this terrible situation. He sent to the college of Montesion, asking Father Alvarez to open a mission in the disorderly town.

Father Alvarez did this. He sent two members of the community to Soller for this purpose. They were Fathers Cosimo Marquez and Matthew Reguer, zealous and deeply spiritual men, and the rector believed that if anyone could help the situation, they could.

Then he bethought himself of a more valued source of aid right at hand. This was the intercession of Brother Alonso Rodriguez.

"Pray, Brother, that peace may soon come to Soller!" the rector commissioned the saintly brother.

Before the altar, Alonso petitioned his Blessed Lord to grant the favor so greatly desired. Then he turned to her through whose tender hands he had received so many favors in the past. He begged the august Queen of Heaven to succor the distraught people of Soller, and stay the ravages of the bandoleros.

As if a living voice answered him from the throne where the lovely Queen held court with her Son, he was assured that peace would come on a certain day, and at a certain hour.

Alonso went in search of Father Alvarez and told him the welcome news, adding: "Father, the mission being given by our our two Fathers will be entirely successful."

Father Alvarez thanked God and the august Virgin for

the happy assurance, and also for giving to the community such a valued and privileged servant of His as Brother Alonso Rodriguez.

Alonso felt an increasing stiffness in his legs as the months succeeded one another, but he went about as if he was not troubled by this infirmity. He was satisfied to leave himself in God's hands and allow Him to do with him as He willed.

He had won many favors from God, and he wished to do much more to bring about the realization of his holy founder's highest dream: God's glory and the good of souls. Another opportunity of satisfying this wish was granted to him, as he stood at the door of the college, one evening. His companion at the time was Father Vincent de Arcaina, a professor who had come to Majorca a short while before to teach grammar, philosophy and theology at Montesion.

Alonso saw two novices, coming through the courtyard. He knew that they must have arrived very recently, for he had never seen them before. He had heard that four students were to land at Palma that day, to continue their studies in the Company.

He asked Father Arcaino: "Who are these two, coming through the courtyard, Father?"

Father Arcaino replied: "They are two new novices, Juan de Humanes and Pedro Claver."

Father Arcaino nearly lost his footing when he heard Alonso's next remark: "These Brothers will go to the Indies, and will reap great fruit of souls," he said.

Father Arcaino had not much experience in dealing with Alonso, since he had been only a short time at Montesion. He was soon to learn much about him.

Alonso fixed his eyes on the face of one of the two young Jesuits, Pedro Claver.

Claver, as if by a secret impulse, turned immediately and fastened his dark brilliant eyes on the face of the venerable Lay Brother, framed in the doorway.

The two exchanged glances of deep affection and understanding. Then Claver and Juan Humanes passed on.

Father Arcaino noticed the looks, and he wondered what they implied.

Not long afterward, he learned, and thanked God for having sent this favored novice to Palma, to find his future life work through the guidance of Brother Alonso Rodriguez.

XII

THE rector of Montesion, Father Gabriel Alvarez, soon became aware that in the novice, Pedro Claver, he had received a very remarkable youth into the community. As he learned more about this novice, he found, at the same time, that Pedro was strongly attracted to Brother Rodriguez. The rector was well satisfied to foster this friendship, because he knew that Alonso's influence over the young man would result in high things.

Claver had entered the Jesuit Novitiate at Tarragona, in Spain. Now, at the age of twenty-five, he gave promise of future achievements of no ordinary kind, as well as great holiness. He had asked that he might be sent to Palma, if his superiors approved, in order that he might meet the saintly old lay brother, whose fame had spread over the three Jesuit Provinces of Spain. Had he been offered the opportunity of studying in the Roman College, he would have chosen Montesion, because Alonso was in the latter place.

As soon as possible, the new novice met Alonso. As if by mutual instinct, the two religious embraced one another.

Father Alvarez had given permission to Claver to spend fifteen minutes each day in the company of Brother Rodriguez, in order to listen to his counsels and imbibe the atmosphere of his great virtues. Alonso, on his part, was overjoyed to be given the privilege of guiding Claver. In his first conference to him, he spoke of the glorious apostolate of the foreign missions of the Indies. Claver was deeply impressed by the thought of the zeal and fortitude of so many Jesuits who were working in this field, and Alonso could see that the idea appealed to him.

One day, when the new novice was going out for a walk with the lay Brother, Michael Serra, Alonso met the two and said to them:

"You are going for a walk? Remember that on one side is Jesus, and on the other Mary."

As the Brother and the Novice sat on a stone bench in the patio of the College one noon, Alonso felt that the time had come to definitely point the way to the far-off Indies, to which he believed God was calling Pedro Claver.

The day was mild, with a tropical breeze blowing bubbles on the curling waters of the bay. The fronds of the palm and carob trees stirred lazily at its breath, as it bore the tones of the monastery bell from near-by Santa Clara above the aromatic herbs and flowers.

Rising at length from the bench, and pointing across the sunflecked bay, Alonso said to Claver:

"See, Brother, how the field is white to the harvest, while there are few reapers to gather it! Look where your brothers in the Company beckon you to come over and help them win to our Blessed Lord countless hordes of poor uncared-for-pagans! Will you answer the call and follow where He beckons? It is a missionary life of labors and dangers, but it is a glorious destiny for one whom God calls. For you, who are so dear to my heart, I ask nothing else. In distant America you will find the opportunities granted to Xavier in the kingdom of the Indies and the Far East."

Claver discussed his vocation with Alonso, and reached the decision to ask permission to go to spend his life among the pagan peoples of the Indies.

He applied to his superiors, then, with Alonso, he waited

patiently, hopefully, for the response. It came, promptly, and stated that the matter of Claver's vocation would be considered when he returned to Barcelona, at the end of his philosophy course at Montesion.

The time of parting between these two ardent friends was not long in coming. The novice begged Alonso never to forget him in his prayers, and Alonso promised always to remember.

With the permission of the superiors, he gave the young man a little folio on religious perfection, which he himself had composed. This was a real concession, for it had become a rule that, although many asked for Brother Rodriguez' writings, none of them were to be taken from Montesion without special reason. Because there were few books to be found in South America, Claver was all the more grateful to be entrusted with such a treasure.

Among the maxims written in the folio were these:

A religious ought to study to know himself, and, knowing himself, despise himself.

He ought to spend little thought for men, but much for God.

He ought always to think the best of others, but the worst of himself.

He ought to be like Melchisedech, without father or mother, without relatives in this world, so that God only may reign in his heart.

He ought to honor the image of God in all men, and to be especially kind to anyone who may offend him, doing good for evil.

Before beginning his actions, the true religious ought to direct all to the greater glory of God, and offer them for the good of his own soul and that of his neighbor.

He should keep God always present in the depths of his heart, in a kind of perpetual retreat, and he should do nothing without consulting Him.

He should employ his senses only in the service of his Saviour, keeping himself free from curiosity, or from distractions which might lead his soul from God. . . .

He should meditate frequently on the four last things, and especially on death; he should labor and suffer, considering that at the last he will have little time to meditate.

He should look on praise as contempt, thinking how hateful pride is to God, and see how much Jesus Christ suffered because of it. He should humble himself in insults and reflect that he has deserved them because of his sins.

In his meditations he should consider the virtues proper to his state, representing to himself the difficulties he may expect to meet in the fulfillment of them, and determine to fulfill them energetically for God.

He ought to cherish a tender devotion to the Most Holy Virgin, and love and serve his Mother with all his heart. He should often in the day visit her altars, recite her rosary and Little Hours, and lose no opportunity of inducing others to imitate her virtue.

Finally, let him direct all he does to God, and he shall find that He will be ever at his side.

Brother Alonso Rodriguez had faithfully practiced these maxims in the years of his religious life. Now he handed them to his young disciple, Brother Pedro Claver, and as he did so, he was privileged to receive a further manifestation of what lay in store for this novice.

It seemed to Alonso that he was led by his Guardian Angel to heaven. There, in a brilliant blaze of light, he saw the thrones of the elect. Each held a shining figure, with the exception of one, which was vacant, although more resplendent than the others.

It was revealed to Alonso that this empty throne was reserved for his favorite disciple, Pedro Claver, as a reward for his great virtues and his heroic labors in winning countless souls to Christ in the mission of the Indies.

Humbly, but joyfully, Alonso told his confessor of the vision. He had not mentioned it to the novice, but now the enlightened confessor stated he had acted wisely in not telling Pedro of it. This new favor served to increase the venerable Brother's zeal in prayer for his young friend.

It was November, 1608, when the two favored Jesuits, Alonso and Pedro Claver, bade farewell to one another, with a tender embrace. One was worn in body as a result of long years of generous sacrifice; the other was fresh and vigorous, with his soul yearning for the crown which awaited him in his chosen life. As Alonso folded the slender boy to his heart, both knew that they would not meet again in this world.

With the novice from Catalonia went Brother Juan Humanes, of whom Alonso had also prophesied that he would serve his Lord in the foreign missions of the Company, and three other novices, Juan Ballester, Antony Gaul, and Pedro Juan Pons. All five took ship in the Bay of Soller, for Barcelona, to prepare for their future apostleship.

Before the end of the year, another spiritual son of brother Alonso Rodriguez left Montesion, never to return. He had come to Palma when Pedro Claver arrived there. He was Jerome Moranta, a native Majorcan.

As he bade adios to Alonso, Jerome gathered up the final words of wisdom that fell from the lips of his revered old friend, to keep sacredly for the remainder of his life. Alonso impressed upon him, as his parting counsel, that the best preparation for his future career in the Company was mortification, humility and a burning zeal for the salvation of souls.

Jerome Moranta carried away with him a little picture of Alonso. In later years, as a missionary, he often showed it to others and told them about his holy teacher, the famous lay brother of Majorca. Eventually, this young man was sent to Mexico. There, by his beautiful life of toil and sacrifice, he won the title of "The Saint." His promising career was cut short when a group of Tepeguani Indians fell upon him and beat him to death with clubs. A Jesuit companion, Father Juan Fonte, a model of modesty and meekness, was martyred with him.

The sacred remains of Father Jerome Moranta were discovered by a group of Spanish soldiers three months after his martyrdom. Beside him, were the remains of Father Fonte, still covered by the hair shirt he had worn during life. Under it was a copy of a sermon he had prepared for the feast of our Lady's Presentation, on the day of his death, November 19, 1616.

When the officer in charge of the squad discovered the hair shirt, he knelt on the earth and venerated the sacred relics of both priests. He then ordered them to be reverently carried to the mission center, where the last rites of the Church were conducted over them. They were then interred with the prayers of the Church in the mission cemetery. Brother Alonso Rodriguez was to learn the story of Fathers Moranta and Fonte approximately one year before his own death.

Now, however, he prayed for the living missioners who were endeared to his generous heart and offered many penances and sacrifices for the success of their work.

Father Alvarez had been recalled to Spain before this time, and his successor, Father Juan Torrens, was in charge at Montesion. Father Torrens became the friend, and also the confessor of Brother Alonso Rodriguez. He frankly stated that he attributed two very special favors he had received to the intercession of Brother Rodriguez. First, he had recovered from a state of ill-health which had rendered him unable to perform the community exercises and duties. Second, he had recovered from a fever, which had attacked him just before he was about to begin a series of Lenten sermons.

When the fever came upon him, Father Torrens was aware, from experience, that it would last for some time. He was about to make arrangements to have another Jesuit take his place in the pulpit when the matter was settled in quite another way.

At the time, Brother Rodriguez was also in poor health. He was confined to his room, and he noticed that the usual visits of the new rector to see him had stopped, and that the Brother Infirmarian seemed to be troubled.

He asked the Infirmarian how Father Torrens was, and was told that he was very ill, so that the doctors had mentioned they were going to bleed him that night.

Alonso began to pray for Father Torrens' recovery, and the Infirmarian left the room. It was later ascertained that at that very time, the rector fell into a quiet sleep, which was unusually long. When he awoke, the fever had disappeared.

Father Torrens got up immediately, dressed, and went down to the chapel, where he said Mass. That evening he opened the series of sermons, as he had planned to do, and continued through the course without suffering a return of his illness.

Father Torrens was heartily in accord with the plan of some of the other Fathers, to have Alonso assist the Novice Master in his duties. They felt that all the young religious in the house would benefit by association with their holy Brother. It was a general procedure for the different Fathers to ask his prayers when they were troubled or in difficulty of any kind.

The results of this confidence were such that the Provincial no longer questioned Brother Rodriguez' way of life. Instead, he cherished the papers Alonso had written at his command, and which Father Alvarez, the former rector at Montesion, had turned over to him, believing they were the inspirations of an elect soul.

The young Brother, now Infirmarian, Antony Mora, was delighted to have the care of Alonso's health at this time. But one day he came to Father Torrens with a disturbed look, and told him:

"Father Rector, just now I went into Brother Rodriguez' room, and I found him resting on the bed, but upright, with no support whatever to his back. I think that is the way he usually rests until he falls asleep. What shall I do, Father? Shall I put him under obedience to lie down at once?"

Father Torrens shook his head.

"No, Brother," he replied. "Don't disturb him. Leave him as he wishes to be."

Brother Mora went away, a little disappointed that the rector had not provided him with the authority to make Alonso take a little comfort for his worn body. But Father Torrens had not given that authorization, and the young Brother could do nothing but obey.

The rector was somewhat amused by Brother Mora's zeal. He had not told him what he really thought about the matter: that their Brother Alonso Rodriguez had support not given to the other members of the community in the same measure.

XIII

THE Christian fleet before Algiers had bowed to the strength of the Moslems, who now dominated the seas. Many Christians had been made captive by these corsairs, among them a number of Majorcans. Some of the captives had been killed, after enduring grave mistreatment at the hands of their masters.

Father Antony Macnamara, a Franciscan, was seized, taken to Algiers and there sold into slavery. He was rescued by a Majorcan vessel and brought to Palma. This incident had occurred in the very recent past.

Father Macnamara had died at Palma, and was buried in the Church of St. Francis. Brother Alonso Rodriguez had often seen his portrait, hanging at the principal entrance to the chapel.

In July, 1605, Vincent de Paul, a missionary, was taken captive off the coast of France, carried off, and sold as a slave in Tunis.

The dangers at sea had not abated. The Jesuits of Montesion, with others, were greatly disturbed when some of their religious had occasion to travel on ships. They had prayed fervently for the safe voyage of the two scholastics, Pedro Claver, and John Humanes, on their way to the American missions. They were relieved and thankful when they learned that the young religious had arrived, unharmed, in America.

At this time, the year 1608, a ship on her way to Alicante from Palermo arrived in the bay of Palma. She was the Velina. On board her was a son of the Marquis of Villena, viceroy of

Sicily, who carried with him some of his father's goods. The vessel also carried a band of musketeers as guard.

Father Torrens, the rector of Montesion, believed that the arrival of this ship afforded an excellent opportunity of sending over to Spain a number of Fathers and Brothers assigned to the colleges in the mainland. He told his consultors his thought and they agreed that it was quite practical. However, it was their opinion that no more than four Jesuits should sail on one vessel in such dangerous times.

Father Torrens was disappointed to hear this. The Jesuits who were expected in Spain had received their assignments, and it seemed that the delay was unwarranted. The rector knew that the Velina was a large ship, quite seaworthy, and well armed.

He decided to consult Brother Alonso Rodriguez, whose lights in prayer were so extraordinary, and find out what he thought about the matter.

He sent for Alonso and told him the story, including the account of the objections raised by the consultors to his plan.

"Pray, Brother," the rector said. "We want to know God's Will in this matter. Then come back and tell me what you have learned."

Alonso went directly to the chapel, as he had done on so many previous occasions when the community was in need of counsel. He began to pray earnestly, asking that the rector might know God's leading in regard to the voyage of the Jesuits.

When he had received the light he sought, he left the chapel and went to find Father Torrens.

He told Father Torrens that if the entire group sailed on the Velina, they would have a "a golden voyage."

Father Torrens thanked Alonso, and remarked that he would be well satisfied if all the Jesuits going to Spain in the next twenty years could embark on that vessel.

He then called his consultors together for the second time. Without mentioning Brother Rodriguez' name or telling them what he had learned through him, he declared that he had decided to send the entire group on the Velina on this voyage. He discussed with them as to whether he should send, also, three postulants, after admitting them to their probation before the time of sailing. This question had already come up. Now it was settled that the postulants should be admitted and join the others on the voyage.

Father Blaise Bailo, who had held the post of professor of philosophy at Palma for the past five years, had recently completed his course there. All his students were ready to go to Valencia, to begin their studies in theology in the College of St. Paul. Father Bailo, Father Pedro Planes, a newly-ordained priest, and these students were in the group who were to embark on the Velina. In the order of their reception into the Society, the scholastics were: Jose Fuente, Humphrey Serra, Antony Marques, Gabriel Alegre and Jerome Lopez. The three newly-admitted Novices were: Raymond Gual, Juan Alcove and Jerome Lopez. A young man who had formerly studied at Montesion, Michael Sancelone, had joined the group. This young man was going to Spain to seek admission into the Society from the Provincial.

Only one member of the band of young Jesuits had given cause of dissatisfaction to his superiors. He was Jerome Lopez. He had entered very young, but he had not proved himself a satisfactory novice. Yet he had received the frequent corrections administered to him with such humility and good spirit that it was believed he would eventually overcome his defects. Jerome had taken his first vows at Tarragona, in 1606, and, after making a brilliant course in rhetoric, was sent to Palma to study philosophy. There he had shown himself very careless in the performance of the duties of his religious life. In consequence of this, the Provincial had ordered Father Torrens to send him back to Spain, at the first opportunity. Father Torrens had tried to induce the Provincial to permit Jerome to remain at Montesion. He had failed in the attempt. The rector had reason to think that, when the Provincial saw and talked with Jerome, he would dismiss him, and he had hoped to avert this action.

When he was called from his studies to hear this verdict, Brother Lopez faced the issue squarely. He wanted to remain at Montesion, and he was determined to improve. But he knew the rector had no alternative but to return him to Spain. So he was told to go on to the port of Soller and take passage on a brig which was waiting there, and which would sail some time before the Velina.

While the scholastic was on the way to Soller, Brother Alonso Rodriguez approached Father Torrens with an important communication. In prayer, God had revealed to him that if Brother Lopez were to set out on this brig, he would be taken captive, with all the others on board, by the Algerine corsairs.

Unhesitatingly, the rector accepted this word. He sent after Brother Lopez, ordering him to return to Montesion at once. He did so, and now he was waiting to set sail with the group of Jesuits going on the Velina.

Due to unfavorable winds, the Velina remained in port until the day after the Feast of the Immaculate Conception. On the ninth day of the month, however, she sailed proudly out of the bay. She had scarcely sailed past the first headland, when another ship passed her. By way of showing that they were in very high spirits, the raw recruits on the Velina fired on the other ship. She did not retaliate, but continued on her course, after giving a broadside.

When the Majorcans heard the booming of the guns, they were greatly disturbed. The viceroy was notified, and he gave an alarm. He ordered some cavalry to go by land, and some frigates by sea, to aid the Velina, which he believed to be in trouble.

When the frigates caught up with the Velina, they found that all was well.

After the departure of the frigates from Palma, the rumor that the Velina had been taken spread throughout the city. It caused the gravest concern to the community at Montesion, as Fathers and Brothers gathered about the rector to discuss the possible events at sea.

As usual, Brother Rodriguez was dispatched to the chapel to petition that all might be well with the absent ones.

As he knelt before the altar, he seemed to see a picture of the ship, proceeding safely and happily on her course, until she had passed the rock-bound island of Ibiza. She then passed out of the range of his inner vision.

Filled with alarm, he went back to Father Torrens and told him what he had seen.

The rector was somewhat disturbed that Alonso had not been able to see the successful ending of the voyage. Yet he recalled that the saintly old Brother had prophesied a "golden voyage" for the Jesuits who had sailed.

As all the community awaited the hoped-for news of the safe arrival in Spain of their beloved brethren, a series of momentous incidents was happening to the ship.

Reaching the coast of Spain, off the town of Denia, about sixty miles north of Alicante, on December fourteenth, she found that the wind had turned against her, and she was unable to enter the port.

As she waited for more favorable conditions, she was surrounded by three Turkish men-of-war, which seemed to come up out of the sea, in a thick fog.

The commander of the enemy fleet was a former Calvinist, a brigand who had taken service with the Turks. He hated the Christian name and all Christians, and he ordered his men to fire on the helpless Velina. They did so, damaging her so badly that it was impossible for her to get away.

All on board knew that one of two terrible fates awaited them: slavery or death.

Many of the passengers and crew of the Velina had been wounded by the Turkish guns. Fearlessly, Fathers Bailo and Planes went among them, administering the last Sacraments to the dying and soothing the others. The younger religious carried food and ammunition to the crew.

Three times the Spaniards succeeded in driving the Turks

back. But the conflict was too unequal for them to hope for victory. When at last the greater number of her musketeers and many of her passengers lay dead, the Velina was forced to surrender.

The commander of the Turkish fleet was angry that he had been forced to delay his conquest by a prolonged encounter. He boarded the Velina, his sword in his hand, and, going among the survivors, killed all whom he found armed with weapons. The others, including the Jesuits, were huddled in the ship's hold.

A passenger had begged the priests and scholastics to put off their religious garb, because, he said, the Turkish leader would doubtless dispatch them at once if he found them wearing it, or, at least, demand an enormous sum for their ransom.

Father Bailo, as the senior priest, replied calmly that they would not do this, because they belonged to the Company of Jesus, and their dress was the symbol of their noble calling.

When the Turkish commander came upon the Jesuits, he ordered his men to bind their hands and feet, and leave them where they were. For four days they remained there, with only a little black bread and fetid water, and, now and then, a morsel of raw fish which was thrown to them, as their sustenance.

When the Turkish vessels reached Algiers, the Jesuits were left in their miserable dungeon an entire week longer. So great were the miseries they endured during this period, that the young aspirant to the Company, Michael Sancelone, died.

Christmas Day was passed in the ship's hold. The two priests did their best to encourage and console their younger brethren, taking turns in leading them in prayer and exhortations to patience and fortitude. They rejoiced to find that no one complained against the Providence which had permitted their capture and subsequent sufferings.

At the end of a week the prisoners were released from their hole and taken on shore. There an auction block was set up, and, one by one, they were sold to the highest bidders.

When they stepped on shore, however, a brave-souled priest, a Catalan, who had chosen to remain in Algiers to minister to Christian captives, came to greet them and did what he could to assuage their fears and burdens.

The scholastics and novices, who had borne up well until now, began to suffer violent temptations to despondency, so that Fathers Bailo and Planes had all they could do to sustain their courage.

Many days after these happenings, the report of the capture of the Velina reached Montesion. It struck like a thunderbolt into the midst of the community, and plunged all into deepest sorrow.

Two members felt the shock most severely because of their intimate share in the proceedings which had proved to be so tragic and deplorable. Father Torrens and Brother Alonso Rodriguez knew that the other Fathers and Brothers regarded them as the unfortunate cause of the catastrophe. The rector had subsequently told them of Brother Rodriguez' vision. He had rejected the counsel of his board of advisers, accepting, instead, that of an old and lowly lay brother.

Brother Alonso Rodriguez knew that he was regarded as the principal factor in the misfortune, although he was innocent of the slightest wrong. Bowed down in misery, he turned to God:

"Why, O my God, did You ordain that so many of ours should now be in such trouble and affliction, in Algiers?" he asked, in all simplicity.

The response was forthcoming immediately. A voice assured him that the voyage of the captured Jesuits would actually be "golden," since it would purify them and try them by fire. In this way, the dross of faults and imperfections would be burned out.

The voice continued: "For the sake of your prayers, I will watch over all these brethren, and in My good time will bring them out of Algiers, without loss to themselves or to the order. Moreover, their captivity will be the source of spiritual profit to many, and to some the means of salvation. They will gain for their souls, and they will not suffer injury."

This heavenly communication was to be verified shortly, as all at Montesion were to learn.

No member of the captive Jesuit band died in Algiers. While no direct word of the group reached Palma for a time, it was felt that they were safe and out of danger.

However, some of the Fathers of the college were now gravely in doubt as to whether, from the first, Brother Rodriguez had been suffering from delusions in his "revelations."

Father Torrens, also, came in for his share of discredit. Some of his companions accused him of culpability in having listened to a decrepit lay brother, rather than to them. So severe were these recriminations that Alonso himself began to fear lest he might have been deceived and victimized by an evil spirit.

But as soon as he had taken his trouble to God, a ray of light struck into his soul, enabling him to perceive that he had not been deceived; that he never could be deceived, because God was leading him for His ends.

Comforted, yet still grieved that he had brought trouble on his friend and Father, the kindly rector, Alonso went about his daily duties as best he could. He prayed constantly for the captives in Algiers, members of his own dear Company. He wrote them many encouraging letters, and waited in confident trust for good news of them.

The most luminous answer to these prayers came during a night vigil. He saw the ten Jesuits now in Algiers, shining with brilliant light. The Fathers and older Brothers among them were renewing their vows, according to the custom of the Company. Now it was made clear to Alonso that their captivity in a hostile land was to be the means of gaining many souls to Christianity.

Brother Alonso Rodriguez could not know at this time how his vision was being justified. Brother Jerome Lopez, who had given some cause for apprehension to his superiors, and Brother

Humphrey, his companion scholastic, had been made slaves in the house of a renegade Spaniard. While there, Brother Lopez had instructed a woman who, once a Christian, had abandoned her Faith and married a Turk, but who had still cherished her religion in her heart. Brother Lopez counseled and aided her until he could entrust her to Father Bailo, who secretly heard her confession and gave her Holy Communion. Brother Lopez had undergone a marvelous change as a result of the edification given by the example of his companions in their trial. His future life in the Company was to reveal a glorious record of nearly forty years of missionary labors, as he journeyed through Spain and preached in thirteen hundred of its villages and cities. In the priesthood of this young Jesuit alone the prophecy of Brother Rodriguez was to be marvelously borne out. The voyage on board the Velina would indeed be "golden" for this youth, and for his companions.

The word of the capture of the Jesuits had reached the ears of the Father General of the Company at Rome, Father Claudius Aquaviva. He learned, too, of the part Brother Alonso Rodriguez had played in the circumstances, and he found himself confronted with a serious and delicate situation. It involved a venerable lay brother, said to possess extraordinary power with God, but who seemed to have brought about the misadventures of the Jesuit band in Algiers. The rector of Montesion, Father Torrens, had acted on the word of this lay brother, in preference to that of his skilled advisers.

Father Torrens was aware that the General was expecting a full accounting from Brother Rodriguez, through him. So he told Alonso to write out a clear statement of his part in the affair. He knew that Alonso believed that what seemed to some others a grave misfortune, was in reality a favor from God, since it had led the Jesuits into a heathen country where they were able to practice their priestly and religious duties, and to win many conversions from Moslemism.

As soon as he had received the obedience from Father

Torrens, Alonso retired to his little room, and began the composition of his letter to the Father General.

He wrote in forthright fashion, in the slightly involved and repetitious style characteristic of him. The letter was addressed to His Paternity, at the Generalate of the Society in Rome.

Alonso wrote:

Pax Christi.

My very dear Father, so great is my lowliness that I should not have ventured to write this, unworthy as I am to speak to Your Paternity. However, as holy Obedience has ordered me to do so, I do it. . . .

As God, by holy obedience, ordered it, and as it is His holy Will, I affirm that the captivity of our Fathers and Brothers is not to be looked on as a misfortune, but as good fortune; not as adversity, but as prosperity; not as trouble, but as comfort and repose; and they themselves will hereafter recognize this better, from the great good they will have drawn from this tribulation, and they will see what a favor God has done them in allowing them to be carried away prisoners to Algiers, for the glory of God and the salvation of souls who are living there, and for their own, with the grace of God. In the Missions hereabouts, there is no danger of denying one's faith, while in Algiers there is. And so it is a great act of charity to aid the Algerines with the help of ours, and the grace of God.

Therefore, we ought to look upon this trouble as a piece of good fortune which has come from the hand of God, and not as a misfortune. . . . Fortunate mission, sent forth, not by the hands of men, but by God Himself! . . .

This will prove a source not only of increase to the Company but will add to its lustre and will further it in its charity and love of God and of its neighbor. . . .

It is one thing to see our troubles with the eyes of the world and of the flesh, but far different to see them in the spiritual light, according to God. . . .

The way of the Cross suffered for God is the way of heaven, and there is a greater difference between adversity suffered for God and prosperity, even in holy things, than there is between a piece of gold and all the lead in the world. . . .

By means of adversities and tribulations, through the grace of God, man becomes spiritual and holy; he is made imitator of Christ our Lord, for it is by this means that he attains sanctity. Through adversities and trials suffered for God he merits before God great degrees of peace and glory, and his soul can say: "Then I am best when I am worst," that is to say, when I have most troubles. And thus, through many tribulations, it is necessary to enter into the kingdom of God.

I commend myself earnestly to Your Paternity's holy sacrifices and prayers.

Majorca, April 23, 1609.

When Father Torrens had read the entire letter Brother Alonso Rodriguez had written to the Father General of the Company, his face wore an inscrutable expression. He did not express his convictions to Alonso on the subject of its contents.

But he felt that the Father General of the Company, the illustrious and renowned successor of Father Ignatius Loyola, youngest son of the Duke of Atri, in the central house of the Company at Rome, would have something to think about when he had read it.

XIV

IN THE hope of obtaining the release of the captive Jesuits in Algiers, the aid of Pere Coton, confessor of Henry IV of France, was enlisted in their cause. At this very time, a representative of the outlaw commander who had effected the capture was in Paris, seeking to win pardon for his master, whose behavior had outraged all Christian leaders. The king knew the circumstances attending the taking of the Velina, and he ordered that a free pardon be granted to the infidel leader, on condition that the Jesuits should be given their liberty.

The corsair could not possibly comply with this condition, because he had sold the ten Jesuits into slavery, and he had no money to pay as ransom for them.

Despite this, Pere Coton continued his efforts. He induced the

Spanish Queen, Margaret of Austria, to help him, and through the generous ransom which she, together with the Duke of Lerma and the Jesuit superiors of the Aragon Province, raised, negotiations were completed. The amount to be paid was agreed upon by Pere Coton, Father Bailo, the superior of the band of Jesuits, and the slave masters.

The price of the ransom of one of the novices, Brother Alcove, had already been paid by the Trinitarian Fathers of the Order for the Redemption of Captives. But the Algerian authorities refused to release him until the daughter of one of the city officials, who was then in Corsica, should be restored to her father.

This girl had become a Christian, and she could not be persuaded to return to her home. So Father Bailo heroically resolved to send the other eight Jesuits away, while he remained to comfort and encourage the novice, Brother Alcove.

Father Planes and the others pleaded that they ought not to leave their companions behind. It was necessary for Father Bailo, in his role of superior of the band, to order their departure as an obedience, before they could be persuaded to go.

Eight Jesuits, one priest and seven Brothers, set sail for Valencia in a French vessel. Adverse winds carried the vessel to the shores of Majorca, instead of to Spain. So they decided to land at Palma and tell the community at Montesion about their adventures since their embarkation on the Velina.

Brother Alonso Rodriguez had received intimation from on high that the former captives would be driven to the shores of Palma. When he met and embraced them, he asked them: "How was it that you wanted to pass by without giving us the joy of meeting and speaking with you?"

One of the community at Montesion knew what Alonso meant, for the Brother had told him, long before the vessel bearing the former captives reached the bay, that they were on their way. He stated that he had seen them coming, under the shelter of our Lady's arms. One of the younger Fathers of the community, Father Marimon, who as a novice a few years before had been a disciple of Alonso's, and had since become his confessor, knew that this revelation was but one of many granted to his penitent, and he was not surprised to have it verified.

The former slaves, now at Montesion, reached Palma on November 3, 1609. They were clothed in the poor garments of slaves, the same they had worn in servitude in the houses of their masters. They were unable to change into their religious habits before sailing, because their passports described the garments they presently wore, and they would not have been allowed to embark had they worn different dress.

Joy reigned supreme in the College of Montesion as Fathers and Brothers of the Community gathered about their rescued brethren and congratulated them on their deliverance with all the warmth of respect and affection. A *Te Deum* was intoned in the community chapel in thanksgiving for their safety.

Father Torrens watched Brother Alonso Rodriguez closely. He was afraid that the weight of suspicion under which he had fallen, and now the relief experienced in finding the religious safe, would further impair his health. Alonso had borne his strong trial meekly, but the rector knew that his deep-seated love for the community would cause him to suffer very keenly, as he realized that some were not in complete sympathy with him. Now Father Torrens was cheered to see the aging Brother, embracing the returned Jesuits with a countenance beaming with joy and devotion.

One of the former captives was a novice recently admitted to the Company. He was Brother Juan Anglada, a native Majorcan. This novice had been permitted to visit his family to console and delight them, after his long absence. But he had no sooner joined the family circle than his father began a carefully prepared campaign to remove him from the Company. However the boy had joined his companions on the ship after the visit.

Father Torrens had learned of the family interference. He

spoke of it to Alonso, with the request that he pray for the security of the novice's vocation.

"Brother," the rector said, "now is the time to pray for Brother Anglada. At this very time he is opposing his father, who wants to take him from us by force."

Without hesitating, Alonso replied: "Be quite at ease, Father. Take your rest in peace. Brother Raymund is in the arms of our Lady. She has taken him under her protection, and she can conquer all of hell. Your Reverence may be as sure of Brother Raymund's victory as if you saw it with your own eyes."

The following morning, despite Alonso's prediction, Father Torrens had a very bad moment in connection with this novice.

Father Ignatius Blanch came to him with the disquieting news that Brother Anglada had been taken from the ship by main force and brought to his home. He had heard that Father Planes and the other former captives had sailed on for Valencia, but that Brother Anglada was not with them.

The rector told Alonso about this. Alonso answered:

"No. It is not so. Raymund has not lost anything, but, rather, gained. Let us thank God and our Blessed Lady, who have won a wonderful victory for him. He is back with the others on board the ship, firm and constant as a rock. Very shortly Your Reverence will see him here, and we shall celebrate his triumph before the brig which is about to take him to Spain, sails."

Father Torrens learned that the report of the ship's sailing, and without Anglada, had been false. For the entire group on board returned to the college the next morning to pay a final visit to the community at Montesion before leaving the shores of the island. Brother Raymund Anglada was with them.

The thought and prayers of all were with the two courageous religious who had remained in Algiers, Father Bailo and Brother Juan Alcove. Soon the glad tidings reached Palma that they, also, had been released.

If any other Jesuit at Montesion was as happy as Alonso to find that the voyage of the Velina had proved to be a "golden one," it was Father Torrens, who had never doubted the truth of the prediction. Even so, there were some Fathers in the house who continued to think that the whole affair was a tragedy. The rector did not try to dissuade them from their opinion. He believed that God would vindicate the gentle-souled humble man, who had never questioned his superiors or companions' estimate of him, but continued in his way of obedience and penance.

Alonso had long before begun his practice of writing down the inspirations and favors granted to him on worn scraps of paper found about the house. In order to secure possession of these papers, after he had written upon them, some of the community, his stanch supporters, made use of a ruse. One of the customs of the house was that the names of all the community should be posted in a conspicuous place at the door. Occasionally, some Jesuit would ask the venerable Brother to give him a paper bearing his name in his own handwriting, so that it might be placed at the door, as if the one already posted had been obliterated or lost. Alonso never went so far as to wonder why the request was made so often, or what had become of the slips of paper he had previously given, on request. But all these little souvenirs were jealously guarded and treasured in secret, as the mementoes of a saint.

At the beginning of August, 1609, the term of Father Ponce de Leon as Provincial of Aragon came to an end. His successor was Father José de Villegas, a native of Castile. The change was to have a very significant effect on the life of Brother Alonso Rodriguez, and greatly add to the burden of his increasing age and infirmity, and the halfhearted attitude adopted by a few of the Jesuits at Montesion in relation to his revelations.

The new Provincial brought with him to Montesion a novice named Francis Colin. This young man was to become one of Alonso's privileged disciples, and in later years, his biographer. Several other young Jesuits were with them.

Father de Villegas had scarcely reached Montesion when he

disclosed to Father Torrens his intention of instituting a thorough and rigorous scrutiny of the character and religious life of Brother Alonso Rodriguez.

Father Torrens was startled and dismayed. While he felt that the beloved Brother would emerge triumphant from such a scrutiny, it grieved him that one so faithful, and now so weakened in health, should have to go through such a harsh proceeding.

The investigation began. All the written articles of Brother Rodriguez were brought to the Provincial, privately, by the rector, and by any of the other Fathers who possessed them. Unhappily, Father de Villegas started his examination of them in a somewhat prejudiced state of mind. He had not forgotten the sufferings undergone by the former Jesuit captives in Algiers, but it seemed that he failed to recognize what great good had been won through it, as well as the fact that Alonso's prediction had come true.

When he had read all the writings of the Brother, in this very prejudiced state of mind, he concluded that a goodly number of members of the community at Montesion had appraised them quite beyond their merits.

He disclosed his verdict to the rector. Then he expressed his strong disapproval of the keeping of any of Alonso's writings as souvenirs.

After the rector had received this order, it was Alonso's turn to receive it. The Provincial called him, and gave him a positive prohibition in the matter of writing down any of his thoughts or "inspirations."

Father Torrens rightly believed that he himself was more deeply grieved than Alonso over this injunction. He had no fears that the obedient Brother would transgress. The order would be obeyed, in all simplicity and sincerity. However, the kindly rector felt that Father de Villegas was waiting for a further opportunity of testing Alonso, and that it would not be a pleasant circumstance when he did so.

Noticing how worn and patched Brother Rodriguez' habit had become, some of the Fathers, including the rector, had said that he should have a new one. In his great love of his vow of poverty, Alonso had begged to be allowed to keep the old one.

Now, however, the rector decided that Alonso ought not to be seen by the Provincial in the worn habit, and he ordered the Brother Tailor to make him a new one.

One last faint plea had received no recognition from Father Torrens: "But, Father," Alonso said, "I am an old man now, and soon I shall be dead. Don't you think, Father, it is useless to give me any new clothes? My old habit is more suited to my present state."

Despite the protest, the Brother Tailor was told to go to work on the new habit. He did so, and when it was finished, gave it to Alonso. In putting it on, the latter did not notice that it was as long as the habits worn by the priests of the Company, whereas the rule required that the habits of the lay brothers should be six inches shorter than the others. Too, Alonso was growing very stooped, and this fact made the habit come still closer to floor.

Before Father Torrens met Alonso, wearing his new outfit, the Provincial met him.

He immediately issued a summons to all the Fathers and Brothers to assemble in the community room. He then sent for Alonso.

When the Brother stood before him, Father de Villegas said to him, in a stern voice:

"What are we to think, Brother Rodriguez, of one who has been so long in the Company, and who ought to be a source of edification to the whole house and a pattern of virtue to all, but who, on the contrary, is a disedification and scandal?

"What idea will our young men have of the observance of the rule when they see the oldest Brother in the house with a long habit? What are they to think of humility when they see him, trying to put himself on a level with the priests? What idea will they have of poverty, when they see him with a smart new habit, as if, after so many years in the Company, he has not learned to despise the vanities of the world?

"Is not all this contrary to the advice he gives others by word of mouth and by writing? And how is this, that a lay brother wastes so much time in writing, although this work is exclusively that of priests, as the work of lay brothers is to see to the care of the house?

"Accordingly, I order the Brother Infirmarian to bring to my room this Brother's writings, and for the future I order him never to take a pen into his hand for anything whatsoever, except in such matters as I shall leave noted down for the Father Rector.

"And now, I desire that the Brother Tailor bring his scissors and cut down Brother Rodriguez' habit to what is prescribed by the rule."

As the Brother Tailor approached, reluctantly, to carry out the Provincial's command, Alonso stood quietly and meekly in the center of the room. The Brother Tailor went through his task with fingers that trembled a little. It was hard for him, and for the others, to see the venerable servant of Christ humiliated, even though he and they knew that Alonso was happy to suffer, believing it was his desert.

There were not a few very uncomfortable Jesuits in the room during the performance. Father Torrens led them all in this respect. He squirmed in his chair, his lips compressed and his heart overflowing with sympathy and affection for Brother Alonso Rodriguez, who was aged and ailing and perfectly innocent of any fault in the matter of the long habit.

The rector was relieved to see Alonso quite composed in his trial. He could not blame the Provincial for putting him to the test, because, for one thing, Father de Villegas did not know the saintly old Brother as did those who lived with him. And, even so, Father Ignatius Loyola, now Blessed Ignatius Loyola since his beatification in 1609, had bade his sons seek humiliations, in imitation of their divine Saviour, who became "a worm and no man" for the salvation of the world.

The illustrious founder of the Society of Jesus had suffered, even to being cast into prison for what others deemed his folly, and to being stoned by street gamins, who mocked his limping gait and his lowly sackcloth. Yet in his actions and example he had carried out the norms he proposed to others who wished to win Christ: the third degree of humility:

> . . . for the better imitation of Christ, our Lord, and the more actual likeness to Him, I wish and choose . . . reproaches, with Christ laden with reproaches more than honors — and I desire to be accounted a good-for-nothing and a fool for Christ's sake, who before me was held for such, rather than wise and prudent in this world.

With a sober countenance and a little pain tugging at his heart, the boy Infirmarian at Montesion, Brother Antony Mora, prepared to carry out the Provincial's orders, to collect all writings Alonso had in his possession, and bring them to Father de Villegas.

Brother Alonso Rodriguez obediently and cheerfully gathered the many scraps and torn pieces of paper on which he had set down his holy thoughts, and handed them to his young friend.

The Brother Infirmarian received them thankfully, and carried them to the Provincial. Antony wished that he could, without soiling his conscience, abstract one little scrap from the pile. He wanted to keep it as a memento of one whom he believed was very holy, and who was not long to be on earth. But he was an obedient religious, and he knew this would be wrong. So he resigned himself to the inevitable, with a little sigh. As he went about his routine duties, he felt that he had somehow, borne a little of the brunt of Brother Rodriguez' unmerited punishment.

For the first time in his religious life, Alonso felt that a prohibition was very hard to accept. His zeal for God's glory and the salvation of souls pressed him to do all he could to add his contribution to that made by great souls in the Company, past and present. He was afraid he would forget some of the lights received from God; that God would blame Him for doing so. Yet he realized that obedience was all there was for him right now, or at any future time. The temptation to think that God wished him to go on writing was overcome, but only after many a long struggle.

He recalled that, only a short time before his admission into the novitiate, he had listened to the plea of the hermit of San Mateo, and, as a result, nearly lost his vocation to the Company. He had promised his first Jesuit confessor, Father Lewis Santander, that he would never again do his own will, but abhor and distrust it. This recollection served to bring back peace to his sorely oppressed heart.

Father de Villegas had not said anything on the subject of keeping little articles that had been used by Alonso as souvenirs of his holy soul. The younger religious at Montesion were thankful that he had not done so, and they had no qualms of conscience when they carefully secreted little articles, such as the scraps which had fallen from the new habit as the Brother Tailor cut it down. Father de Villegas had seen them taking up these shreds, but he had believed they were doing so in order to clear the floor of debris. All in all, from the rector to the youngest Brother in the house, no one thought that the presence of the Provincial had brought a ray of sunshine with it. Yet they knew he was a holy and zealous man.

Several of the lay brothers at Montesion had not obtained much education in the schools before entering religious life. With the approbation of his superiors, Brother Rodriguez was happy to assist them, so that they could become more helpful to themselves and to the Company. The former business experience he had enjoyed in the world was of great use at Montesion, as it had been at Valencia.

Father Jose de Villegas bade farewell to the Fathers and Brothers at Palma, after a short but uncomfortable visit, and sailed for Spain. Father Torrens jokingly remarked to another

Father that there seemed to be more smiles on certain faces after that. But he did not refer to Alonso, who would not have wished the Provincial to go away.

The Provincial reached Spain without mishap, and entered on his duties there. But one day, not long afterward, the word came to Montesion that he was dead. All offered prayers for his repose, and a number of Masses were celebrated for that intention in the church and chapel of Montesion.

Meanwhile, Father Torrens, released from his office of rector, became Alonso's spiritual guide, with Father Marimon acting as his regular confessor. Father Torrens knew the soul of the holy Brother as no one else knew it. When Alonso told him that it seemed as if he was pressed to continue his spiritual writing, Father Torrens decided that, for the time being, it would be well for him to refrain from doing so. He had a very good idea that the new rector, Father Gil, would think well of allowing him to continue but he did not wish to anticipate the permission. Too, he was aware of the wishes of the late Father Provincial Jose de Villegas. He told Alonso that God would make up for the deficiency in the matter of his writing.

The new rector of Montesion, Father Gil, had no sooner learned the ways of the house and the nature and extent of his duties, than he inquired about Brother Alonso Rodriguez. He was told what had occurred during the recent visit of the late Provincial. Father Torrens simply stated the facts, making no recommendation whatsoever to Father Gil.

But Father Gil was a man of broad sympathies and unusual enlightenment. When he ascertained in minute detail all that had happened in relation to the former captives of Algiers, he told Father Torrens that he believed the Brother should be permitted to resume his interrupted journal.

Delighted beyond measure with the permission, Alonso immediately went looking for every available cast-off scrap of paper he could find. Brother Mora, dancing about with joy as he heard the glad news, gave him more than one hint of the location of available scraps. Alonso would find them, then carry them to Father Gil to ask his permission to keep and use them.

All the community at Montesion knew the history of their new rector. Before entering the Company, Father Gil had won distinguished honors for brilliance of achievement. As a Jesuit he had been, first, professor of Divinity at Barcelona, then three times the rector in that city. Father Gil was much pleased to allow Brother Rodriguez to continue in his accustomed apostolate among the students of the college. As a result of it, vocations increased. At one time, twelve young men applied for admission into the Company. Father Gil, however, thought it wise to receive only two of them. One of these was a young man over whom Brother Rodriguez was to exercise a remarkable influence.

This student, Mark Antony Puigdorfila, had met with stern opposition to his vocation at home. His family resided in Palma, where they were honored among its most distinguished citizens. Mark Antony had gone through his philosophy course at Montesion but had afterward entered on worldly pursuits. As he immersed himself in one pleasure after another, it was evident that his studies suffered.

When the Provincial discovered that the young man lacked the requisite attainment for his reception into the ranks of novices, he declined to receive him, unless he would consent to go over his entire classical course.

Alonso heard Mark Antony's story, and encouraged him to follow the Provincial's advice. He did so, and began all over the work he had done in the lower classes. As a result of hard application and study, in three months' time he had reached the required average.

He now thought to go over to Spain and consult the Provincial in person about his vocation. When his father learned of this intention, however, he threatened the captain of the ship on which the young man was to sail with dire punishment if he took Mark Antony on board.

The boy returned to Montesion in tears, asking to be kept there. The rector told him to return home, and there wait and pray.

Mark Antony spent seven months in this manner, meanwhile advancing in his studies. At the end of that period, one of his relatives assisted him to escape to Spain, where he was received as a Jesuit novice. After his two years' probation, he was sent back to Palma, to continue his preparation for the priesthood.

Now very happy and successful, Mark Antony often conversed with Brother Rodriguez, who taught him all the precepts of the spiritual life he had taught to so many others.

Father Torrens had long since discovered what Father Gil soon learned — that on the point of religious obedience, Brother Alonso Rodriguez had adopted a firm and unalterable standard for his own behavior. He followed what he was told to do with the utmost exactitude, even in the most insignificant things. Occasionally, as when he had started off for the Indies without hat or coat, this perfection of observance caused the superiors more or less embarrassment, according to circumstances.

In every Spanish city the time of carnival was observed with great gaiety. People from all over the Island of Majorca came to Palma, to participate in it. The devotion of the Forty Hours was held at Montesion during this period, and many of those who came to the fiestas took occasion to visit the church of Montesion to take part in the solemn observance. As a result of this, the church was usually crowded beyond its capacity.

One evening during this time, Father Gil entered the church in order to hear the sermon. He went up into one of the galleries to find a seat. There he found Alonso, seated in a very narrow space.

At once Alonso rose to make room for his superior. But Father Gil said to him, in a low tone: "Keep quiet, Brother! Don't move! Sit down!"

Alonso did so.

The sermon came to an end, and the rector left the sacred

edifice, to return to his business in the house. The Solemn High Mass began, went through its various parts, and came to its close, after which the vast congregation filed out.

The bell for first dinner rang at Montesion, and Fathers and Brothers filed into the refectory. The meal progressed to the end, and the second dinner began.

Father Gil, who came to the second table, took a seat beside one of the faculty, Father Redo. Father Redo, who greatly reverenced Alonso, noticed that he was not present.

He spoke to the rector about his absence, asking him if, perhaps, he had sent Brother Rodriguez on some errand about the house.

"I don't recall having done so, Father," replied the rector.

Father Redo knew Alonso sufficiently well to realize that his absence might indicate something of which the rector was quite oblivious. He asked him: "Father, perhaps you will recall whether you did not say something to Brother Rodriguez which he has construed as an obedience, requiring him to remain in some particular place."

Father Gil reflected for a moment. Then he called a scholastic and told him to go to the church gallery, to see if Brother Rodriguez might be seated there. If he was, he was to come to the refectory at once, as it was the rector's wish he should do so.

The scholastic found Alonso, seated where Father Gil had left him. He gave him the rector's order, and Alonso left the gallery on the instant, not stopping to lay aside his cloak.

With a stolid face, Father Gil welcomed him to the refectory, and told the scholastic to take his cloak, then go and get his cap and zimarra—a loose outer robe worn at that time—and bring them to him.

"Be seated, Brother," Father Gil said, bethinking himself that he must be sure to tell him to rise at the end of the meal. "Why did you stay up there in the gallery, Brother?"

"Because it was an obedience for me to do it, Father."

"But, Brother, when the bell rang for dinner, don't you think that was the call of obedience? Should you not have come down for dinner right away? If you were ordered to stay where you were, as well as come down, your rule tells you that you should have gone to the superior and asked him which of the two calls you should obey. What do you say to that?"

"I can say nothing, Father," Alonso replied, simply.

Father Gil realized that he could find no fault with a religious who obeyed his rule with such scrupulous exactitude.

A little later, Alonso was seated in the small enclosed courtyard of the residence. Although it afforded a superb vista of the sparkling bay, the white-winged ships and the amber hills beyond, he was not looking at them. Nor was he resting his eyes by letting them wander up, up, to the very tips of the palm tree fronds, that seemed to be brushing the cloud cobwebs out of the sky.

Only when Father Gil came into the courtyard did he look up and rise at once.

The busy rector had quite forgotten the incident of the church gallery. He was thinking of several important concerns of his charge. So he said to Alonso: "Keep quiet, Brother! Don't move!"

Then Father Gil sat down on the log which served as seat for Alonso, and talked with him for a little while. When he rose and went into the house, he left the Brother, seated in the same position.

Several members of the community had occasion to pass through the patio in the next few hours. They noticed Alonso, sitting on the log, but they did not know how long he had been there.

Finally, one of the Fathers sensed that he had seen him in the same position some time before. He thought it well to speak to the rector about the matter.

He went to Father Gil's room, and said to him: "Father, Brother Rodriguez is sitting in the place where we hold our recreation, and he does not seem to be going away, although he has been there for hours. Is it because you told him to do it that he is staying there?"

Father Gil experienced a mild shock. He remembered that he had told Alonso not to move from the log.

"Please go, Father" he told the priest, "and tell Brother that he is free to rise, now, and leave the patio. I did tell him to sit there, but I did not mean that he was to stay there forever. Tell him he may go to his prayers and devotions, now."

Later, Father Gil asked Alonso why he had not risen when the bell sounded. He replied, with a deep obeisance: "Because I am a blockhead, Father. I think that is why."

The numerous incidents of this nature which occurred made it clear to the superiors that if Brother Rodriguez was to enjoy any measure of freedom at all, they must exercise great care not to say anything to him which could be interpreted so literally as to cause embarrassment all around.

In a report which Father Gil sent to Rome during his term as superior at Montesion, he declared that Brother Alonso Rodriguez was "of good judgment, of great and heroic prudence, and a man of vast experience, especially in spiritual matters." He likewise testified that he had never seen or heard this Brother violating in the slightest way any order of the house. He stated that he relied upon him absolutely for the perfect fulfillment of any duty he was asked to perform, and that he performed every task to the best of his ability.

Now and then some of the other Fathers brought up the subject of Alonso's "extreme" fidelity to the rule of obedience. But Father Gil always answered in substance to the opinion that it might be a "bother" to superiors:

"It would be a good thing if superiors never had any other bothers."

During the course of a retreat he was giving to the scholastics and lay brothers, Father Gil impressed upon them the importance of strictly adhering to the method of making the Exercises proposed by the Blessed Ignatius Loyola.

Alonso was troubled by this exposition. Later, he told Father Gil that he could not always follow that plan, since, for many years, he had followed a method of prayer which consisted entirely of affections and gratitude for the light granted to him.

The rector answered: "Do as I have told you, Brother. For that is what our Blessed Father Ignatius prescribes."

Alonso tried very hard to comply with the obedience, but he found it almost impossible to follow it. However, for his diligent effort to do so, he received great interior consolations, with the assurance that his fidelity had given pleasure to God, as it had done to his superior.

Father Gil endeavored to lessen or mitigate the severity of the penances which Alonso inflicted upon his body. Finally, the wise rector forbade the aged Brother to use the discipline more than twice weekly, or to stoop in the refectory and kiss the feet of all, as an act of humility and as he had obtained an earlier permission to do.

"If Your Reverence will permit me, I should like to recite the Miserere on my knees in the refectory, with my arms outstretched in the form of a cross," Alonso pleaded.

"You may, Brother," Father Gil conceded. But he repented of having given the permission when he noticed how Alonso's arms drooped with pain and how his body doubled over like a closed jackknife as he made the effort. The sight filled all in the room with edification and compunction for their own weaknesses.

Father Gil also allowed Alonso to "tell his fault" at table every week. He did so most religiously and honestly. But the telling proved to be more of an exhortation than any real revelation of a lack in the soul of the saintly Brother.

Knowing Alonso to be a master in the spiritual life, Father Gil often asked him to give a discourse at the Spiritual Conferences which were held at Montesion on Friday evenings. So profound and so touching were these talks that all the community looked forward to them with the utmost eagerness. The themes on which Brother Rodriguez was most eloquent were the Most Blessed Sacrament of the Altar and the Holy Sacrifice of the Mass.

"Brother Rodriguez teaches us all," the rector affirmed. "His daily life is so filled with modesty, so free from sloth, so recollected, and so entirely given to prayer, and he is so careful of his words and gentle in temperament that he seems like an angel in the house."

Father Gil was accustomed to celebrate the earliest Sunday Mass in the college church. He used to notice the bent figure of Brother Rodriguez, wrapped in the aged cloak, which Father Jose de Villegas, the departed Provincial, had never happened to see, as the Brother knelt in the sanctuary serving Mass. His face, aglow with light, and his eyes filled with unshed tears, he did not seem to know that in winter the winds swept in from the bay, making the church very cold, or that in summer the heat was correspondingly intense.

Father Gil gave Alonso no task to perform about the house, but urged him to divide his time between the instruction of the young Jesuits, writing, prayer and meditation. He particularly told him to commit all his heavenly inspirations and revelations to writing, since now there was no reason for not doing so.

In response to the request from one so dearly beloved, Alonso began his *Memorial,* which was an account of his manifestations of conscience and other matters of a spiritual nature.

With the scratchy old pen which Brother Antony Mora, the Infirmarian, could never induce him to relinquish for a better, he set down many salutary maxims, destined to be of great help to souls long after he had died. Once in awhile, Brother Mora, who never wrote at all, thought that he might get possession of the old pen, when Alonso had no further use for it, and, with Father Gil's permission, tuck it away as the relic of a predestined soul.

Alonso did not relinquish the pen, even though Antony tried

the expedient of insinuating the thought that its scratching might tickle the ears of some of those who had to listen to it, as they passed Alonso's room.

Brother Mora enjoyed very high spirits, but he loved his work of caring for the sick and the infirm of the community. He felt that he was particularly privileged in having the care of Alonso's health and in having free access to the room of the aged Brother.

Sometimes, in cleaning the room or performing other duties there, Antony would come across some of Brother Rodriguez' precious writings, inscribed on a piece of torn paper he had picked out of some rubbish heap, and read what a saint had written:

"Trials are a gold mine, and the more one works this mine, the more gold he gets and the richer he grows. And the way to work it is to mortify and conquer oneself in the eyes of God by interior acts in the heart, speaking with Him and saying to Him: 'Lord, my God, dispose of me and of these trials which I am now suffering, to Thy greater glory, that I may serve Thee better.'

"Then, from the depths of your heart, make acts of love of these trials, and declare that you wish to bear them for God's love; and great treasures and wealth will you gather from this mine, both for soul and body."

XV

THE people of Palma no longer watched the slight figure of Brother Alonso Rodriguez passing along the streets, sometimes as the companion of one of the Fathers of Montesion, sometimes alone, and carrying a basket of food for the sick on his arm. They missed the inspiration of that saintly presence, and the visits of Brother Rodriguez in their homes. The poor, especially, experienced this as a great lack in their burdened lives. Often the Brother had sat beside the poverty-stricken, in their humble abodes, speaking to them of the things of God, while one of the priests of the college was ministering to some ailing member of the household.

In the noble castle of Bellver, on its wooded height above the old city, Dona Jane Paz, now an old woman, thought often of the Jesuit Brother, whom her young nieces, since grown to lovely womanhood, had seen surrounded by flocks of white doves in the patio. Fine mansions, too, felt the privation of no longer welcoming Brother Alonso Rodriguez into their stately galleries and rooms.

Brother Rodriguez would never again leave Montesion to go about the city, although he had still some time left on earth. His frail health and broken body would not permit it, and his superiors, wishing to conserve what strength he had, watched more anxiously as the days went on over this beloved member of their community.

The flimsy buildings of the college and residence of an earlier day were now succeeded by better accommodations, as additions and improvements continued to be made. However, the room assigned to Brother Rodriguez was poorly situated, since it was exposed to the extremes of cold and heat, according to the season. The paved floor was usually somewhat damp, and it was this condition that had brought on a catarrhal trouble from which Alonso had suffered during all his religious life.

One of the Fathers asked him why he thought he so frequently fell ill, and he replied that, as far as he could know, it was the unwholesome air of his room that was responsible for the condition. But, he added, he would not ask for a change, and, in any event, none of the rooms at Montesion were completely satisfactory in this respect. Fathers and Brothers had cheerfully borne the discomfort and inconvenience resulting from such poor living quarters. Alonso knew this, and he remarked to the priest who asked him about his room: "See,

Father, how many others in the College, who were far stronger than I, and better lodged, have died since coming here. There is nothing so important as to leave ourselves in God's hands. He always takes the more pains about us as we take less care of ourselves for His sake."

The superiors decided that it was advisable for Alonso to take "a mouthful" of food every morning, although at that time breakfast was not a regular meal of the day, and the community usually took only a very light portion of food before noon. Father Gil told Alonso of this wish, but he did not intend that his expression, "a mouthful," should be taken so literally as it was.

When Brother Mora, the Infirmarian, found that his beloved patient was taking only that little portion, and no more, he told Father Gil about it. He was instructed to order Brother Rodriguez to take sufficient food to keep up his failing strength.

Alonso obeyed without argument. But Antony noticed that while taking the food he held one foot up from the floor, in order to atone for what seemed to him over-indulgence in the satisfying of his appetite.

On more than one occasion when Alonso visited the kitchen, to obtain this food, he found no one on hand to serve him. In this event he would wait patiently until the Brother Infirmarian appeared, then take gratefully what was given to him.

The Brother Tailor, who had unwittingly caused sorrow to Alonso by making his new habit too long, often received a call from the aged Brother. Alonso would come into his room, smiling, with a pin in his hand, and say: "See, Brother! I found a pin on the floor! I thought you might have use for it."

The Brother Tailor would accept the pin, with thanks, edified at the manner in which Brother Rodriguez kept his vow of poverty.

As he found unwanted or cast-off bits of paper about the house, Alonso continued to take them to the superior, begging permission to make use of them for the continuance of his "*Memorial.*" Father Gil always granted the permission, which was the only favor he had known Alonso to seek. When the paper was given into his keeping, Alonso would limp off, happily, to his room, where, seated at his little table, he would set to work writing down his latest impressions of God's holy grace.

Not seldom Brother Mora would come into his room when Alonso was busy at work on the *"Memorial,"* the sleeves of his habit carefully rolled back so as not to soil them, and the worn-out pen busily scraping the paper.

The Brother Infirmarian would come over to him, and say: "Excuse me, Brother. May I arrange your table?" Or—"May I have a word with you?"

Then Alonso, an eager flush on his thin face, would sit back in his straight hard chair and wait in patience until the task was finished, or listen courteously to what Brother Mora had to say. Meanwhile, the astute young Antony would allow his eye to travel over the writing on the paper. Always it contained something beautiful and inspirational.

The constant pains which he suffered in his stomach and legs made it impossible for Alonso to enjoy much refreshing sleep at night. Brother Mora felt very keenly the fact that he could do nothing to relieve this. Once, when he entered the little room very early in the morning to ask Alonso how he was, the reply was that he had been in torment all night. But Alonso added, instantly: "I have no other remedy but to bear my pains for the love of God, and thank Him for the favor He has done me in giving me this treasure out of His divine charity."

In January, 1613, Alonso caused all the community serious alarm by falling down a flight of stairs leading from the first to the second floor of the residence. He had been preparing to go up to his room, after having spent some time downstairs, reading the rules of the Company to some of the less well educated lay brothers. He had ascended to the top step, when he lost his footing, and plunged down the entire flight to the landing below.

Two of the scholastics had just come to the top of the stairs, preparatory to going down. Horror-stricken, they ran to the aid of Alonso, who had doubled over in his fall and struck his head as he touched the paving stones. One of the young Jesuits lifted him, while the other ran to ring the community bell to summon aid.

When they heard the sound of the bell at an unaccustomed time, most of the Fathers and Brothers in the house hurried to the scene.

Brother Alonso Rodriguez lay insensible in the arms of the first scholastic. On his head were two great wounds, and he seemed more dead than living.

Acting on the rector's orders, the scholastic, Brother Colin, with the help of his companion, carried Alonso to bed. Father Gil, meanwhile, sent for the community physicians. When they arrived, they examined Alonso and agreed that his fall, at such an advanced age, must be fatal.

Brother Colin remained at the bed of the injured Brother all that night. In the morning, since the patient was conscious, he asked him how he felt.

"I have suffered pains as of hell, Brother," was the answer, spoken in a tone of great patience.

Brother Antony Mora had just been assigned to a different post, that of the door, while Brother Carrio, one of the group of lay brothers, had become Infirmarian. When Brother Carrio came to relieve Brother Colin of his watch, entering the sick room, he heard Alonso cry out: "More, O Lord! More suffering for Thy love!"

"What would you like to eat, Brother?" the Infirmarian asked.

"Whatever you wish to give me, Brother."

"All I can do, Father Rector," Brother Carrio told Father Gil, "is to give Brother Rodriguez the things I think are the most palatable, but I know he would prefer to have poor food. I told him it is an obedience for him to eat what I bring, and he does so."

During his illness, Alonso was very anxious lest he should take any medicine or refreshment after midnight on his Communion days. Brother Carrio had to keep on the alert in order not to have him disappointed in this respect. The Infirmarian realized that the medicine left by the doctor for his patient was very nauseating. But Alonso did not mention the fact.

Once, raising himself on his pillow, the sick man said, in a firm voice: "'My grace is sufficient for thee' – Nothing is too much . . . God means to teach me a lesson by allowing me to suffer."

Father Gil spoke to the assembled community about the marvelous fortitude and abnegation of Brother Rodriguez. Both the rector and the physician had forbade him to try to meditate, lest it should hurt his wounded head. He told Father Gil that he found it impossible not to do so, and he was afraid he would disobey orders by thinking of holy subjects. When he explained his difficulty to the rector, he said: "Father, I am trying, but I cannot forget God." Father Gil then told him not to bother whether he could meditate or stop doing so – to be content with whatever came.

Brother Colin, the scholastic who had been the first to raise Alonso after his fall, was permitted to share honors with Brother Carrio in taking care of the sick man. Brother Colin, then twenty-one years old, was happy to receive the permission. He had entered the Society at the age of fourteen, and all at Montesion felt that he somewhat resembled the holy little Luigi Gonzaga, the departed Italian scholastic of the Company. Alonso was deeply devoted to Brother Colin, who in later life was to become a missionary to the far-off Philippine Islands. Alonso had received intimation of the holiness of the scholastic as, one day, he knelt in prayer in the church. Later he told Father Gil what he had experienced:

"I was kneeling, Father, at Mass. When the Holy Sacrifice had come to its end, Brother Colin received Communion with me. At that instant I received so great a light as to his holiness that he seemed to me more than an angel—as if he had risen to the rank of the archangels. Long before that, I had been edified by Brother Colin's fine character and virtues, and he had held a high place in my esteem. How can I tell you, Father, what passed in my soul, when I found myself kneeling beside him at Communion, and saw him so beautiful and holy, while I, so close to him, was so full of sin as not to deserve to be near him?

"The vision of this angelic holiness will be fresh throughout the rest of my life, and will be a motive for me to imitate him. I beg God to help me do so! Although I am so unworthy, Brother Colin will sustain me in my needs."

The office of rector of a Jesuit community had its heavy burdens and responsibilities. In addition to the temporal concerns, which were of the greatest moment, to the rector belonged the responsibility for the entire personnel. Father Gil, besides these duties, now had a new cause for anxiety and effort.

For several years famine had threatened the Island of Majorca. Only three years before this time the scarcity of rainfall had motivated the bishop to ask all the people to unite in prayer during the Forty Hours Devotion, asking God to stay the drought and send rain.

Only one year before, the Jesuits of Montesion had appealed to their congregations, in the Lenten courses of sermons, asking them to help those in distress. A public procession had been held, with the permission of the authorities, asking for rain.

The poor communications existing between Majorca and Spain further promoted the tragic conditions brought about by the crop failure. It seemed that in all the Island of Majorca there would be no harvest. A vast supply of wheat was necessary to tide the citizens over this serious emergency.

February had far advanced without relief. The weeks passed until May, and the struggling crops, especially the corn, which had begun to ripen in the stalks, drooped and withered. The entire supply was lost, although an attempt was made to save at least a little of it. This was used to make some bread, but when it was tasted, it was so bitter that it could not be eaten.

The poor suffered most in the dreadful blight. They were existing largely on carob beans, usually reserved as fodder for the cattle. No grass appeared for miles around. Hundreds died of actual starvation, while many others became very ill.

Father Gil paid a visit to the bishop to make a suggestion. It was that a triduum of prayer and fasting should be opened at once. The rector of Montesion also suggested that processions, such as those held in Majorca on Rogation Days, should be held.

Bishop Bauza gladly acceded to the proposition. In his fervent wish to help, he sold all the fine silver plate in the episcopal residence and gave a great dinner there for more than one hundred poor people. But the situation in general remained as bad as before.

Father Gil believed the time had come to ask Brother Rodriguez to help in a very special way. He called him, and said:

"Pray, Brother! Begin to pray, and do not stop until I tell you the crisis has passed."

It seemed that Alonso had no more than begun his crusade of prayer, when, unexpectedly, two ships, laden with corn, reached Palma. Its cargo came from Spain and other countries of Europe.

Those in command of the vessels had not known of the situation existing at Majorca, and came as if by chance. The following week other, similarly laden, ships arrived at the port of Palma.

Father Gil said nothing to Alonso about the coming of the ships, which he believed God had sent in answer to his prayers. He encouraged him to continue petitioning for help, hoping for new favors.

The hopes were justified. During October and November, rain fell heavily all over the Island, continuing, with short intermissions of clear weather. The resulting harvest was all that could be desired.

Father Gil thought it his duty to make known to all the Majorcans what he felt was accomplished through the meditation of Brother Alonso Rodriguez. He did so, and the veneration of the people for the saintly lay brother was greatly increased.

Although busy in his new duties as porter, Brother Antony Mora was relieved now and then so that he could pay a visit to Alonso in his room.

When first he had been charged with the care of the door, Antony had naïvely said to Alonso: "Father Rector has given me this post, but I don't know how long I shall keep it."

"The keys will not be taken away from you very soon," Alonso assured him.

As he discussed his interior state with his old friend, the young lay brother confided: "I don't feel any difficulty at all in religious life, Brother. It is easy for me to obey, and to perform my duties, whether I am sick, or whether I am tempted. Sometimes I really feel sorry that everything goes so well with me."

Alonso replied: "Prepare yourself, Brother, for God will send you troubles."

This prophesy was fulfilled. But, inspired and helped by the prayers and counsel of his revered friend, Antony happily surmounted them all.

Brother Carrio, the new Infirmarian, was very solicitous to help his patient on every possible occasion. Generally, he remained on duty in the house, and rarely left Montesion. But one day he was asked to go with a priest to visit a poor criminal, then lodged in prison, under the death sentence.

Before leaving the house, Brother Carrio asked the rector to send someone else to care for Brother Rodriguez during his absence.

Father Gil did so. Unfortunately, the brother assigned to the duty did not understand that he was to do more than carry the ailing Brother's supper to him. He did this, and later, removed the dishes and carried them back to the kitchen. He did not return to the sick chamber.

It was customary at Montesion for the mattresses on the beds to be rolled back for airing during the daytime. Alonso's mattress had been rolled back while he was out of bed for a little while. When he wished to get into bed once more, he tried to roll back the mattress, but found he had not sufficient strength to do so. He got into bed, and lay down on the boards, which were covered only by a thin blanket.

At midnight Brother Carrio, who had returned late from the visit to the prison, came into Alonso's room to see whether he needed anything. He was aghast to find the aged Brother curled up on the boards, vainly trying to keep warm. When the Infirmarian touched him, he found that he was quite cold.

Alonso, however, had no complaint to make. "I have spent the night to my heart's content, glory be to God for it all! I shall soon be well, thanks to the Lord!"

To the great joy of all the community, their Brother Alonso Rodriguez made such improvement that he was again able to walk about the house, although very slowly.

He was pleased to find that a new lay brother had been added to the little group of temporal coadjutors at Montesion. He was Brother Escales. This brother soon noticed that at table Brother Rodriguez always tried to ensure that what was least perfect or agreeable, possibly a trifle stale, or under or overcooked, became his share. He was glad that he had been sent to a house where he could enjoy the companionship of such a perfect exemplar of the spirit and rule of Blessed Ignatius Loyola. But Brother Escales did not intend to follow Alonso in that degree of mortification which characterized the former wool merchant of Segovia.

A Father of the community happened to be serving at table one day, when Alonso and Brother Escales were both present. The two lay brothers sat together, and Alonso was most solicitous that everything good should go to his companion, and everything less desirable to himself.

By mistake, a dish containing two raw, stale eggs had been

carried to the table by a Brother, who had taken them from the kitchen, unnoticed by the Brother Cook, who had intended to dispose of them.

The dish was placed before Alonso, who took one and broke the shell.

A Father, who was seated on one side of Alonso, was greeted with the foul odor. Turning to Alonso, he said, without looking at the Brother's plate: "Brother, what is that bad odor I get?" At that moment the Brother Cook, who had missed the eggs, came hurriedly into the refectory. He snatched the plate containing the untouched egg from Alonso's place. But it was too late to reclaim the other. Alonso had taken it.

As, at Montesion, one after another beloved rector was relieved of his charge and assigned to another post, so Father Gil's turn came.

With a lingering sadness, he bade adios to Brother Alonso Rodriguez, certain that they would never again meet on this earth. Alonso was equally affected at the parting, for Father Gil had proved himself, like Father Coch and Father Torrens, a most understanding and mortified superior, whom everyone loved. Both had the consolation of knowing that Father Torrens was still at Montesion, where he was the confessor to the community. Until a new rector was chosen, Father Paul Fons was named to take Father Gil's place.

Although many of the Jesuits whom he had known and revered had gone from Montesion, Alonso did not forget them in his faithful thought and prayers. Each one held a special place in his affectionate regard.

But of them all, the former novice, Pedro Claver, now an ordained priest of the Company, laboring in America, was first and dearest. Like a faint echo left by a bell after it has ceased ringing, came the news of him, and of his great work in the foreign missions of the Company in Spanish-America.

In the beautiful city of Cartagena of the Indies, on the north-west coast of South America, Father Pedro Claver walked amid this rare beauty, but, like his old teacher, Brother Alonso Rodriguez, not seeing it.

In the unholy hovels where miserable slaves lay on wisps of dirty straw; where every sense and sensibility of a man were assaulted by noxious odors of dank death, as the fetid sores of dying Negroes ate into their living putrid flesh, Father Pedro Claver had found his love.

In his heroic labors for the salvation of these poor Negroes, he who chose as his title, Slave of the Slaves, kept two lovely mementoes of his early life in the homeland.

One was the little picture of Alonso, the other the folio containing his writings, which the young saint wore beneath his mean habit. These treasures provided everything beautiful and precious in the life of one who, as his Blessed Father Ignatius counseled, was striving to attain with all his might the end of the Society: "Not only to attain to the salvation and perfection of our own souls, with the divine grace, but with the same earnestly to employ ourselves in procuring the salvation and perfection of our neighbor."

XVI

TIME had weathered the yellow house in the Plaza del Azoquejo, and many of the townspeople who had known the Rodriguez family had departed from this life. But Diego Rodriguez and his family were not forgotten by those of the older generation who lived in the old walled city of Segovia. Strangers, entering, they were often told about the holy lay brother of the Jesuits, now living on the island of Majorca, and astonishing all by the wonders of his perfection and his miracles. Children, passing the quiet house under the chestnut and carob trees, sometimes stopped to gaze in wide-eyed wonder at the windows and loggias, telling one another that it was the home of a saint . . . "He saw the Mother of God!" Or: "The beautiful Virgin wiped his face with her handkerchief!"

Within the spacious rooms of the old mansion, two of the sisters of Alonso Rodriguez still lived their chosen life of consecration to the service of God. Antonia and Juliana Rodriguez were now elderly women, whose secluded manner of living sometimes elicited expressions of surprise, or even disapproval, from those who did not understand such sacrifice.

Antonia and Juliana rose very early in the morning, and, until it was time for the opening of the doors of the Jesuit Church in Segovia, they meditated and recited prayers. They remained in the church for several Masses, then returned home to perform their light household duties, before sitting down to do the mending for the church and residence of the Fathers. In the evening they recited the Rosary together, with other prayers of the Church, then retired to rest, in anticipation of spending the following day in similar works of piety and charity.

Alonso knew that his holy sisters had certain strong trials to undergo, even to persecution, from some of their neighbors of a later generation. The frequency with which they approached the Sacraments was criticized, for at this time the Holy Eucharist was received generally as a form of penance, which must be offered to God at least once a year. Very few Catholics received Holy Communion often; even the members of religious communities did not do so.

The Founder of the Society of Jesus, the Blessed Ignatius Loyola, had deplored this unholy attitude. One of his first acts, as he formed his little company of militant religious, was to impose upon all its members, and all his and their penitents, reception of the Sacraments at stated times, not too far removed from one another. This they were free to do, after earnest and sincere preparation.

When he had composed his book of the Spiritual Exercises in the cave at Manresa, Ignatius wrote into them this injunction: "To praise Confession and Communion made once a year, more if made every month, and much more if made every week, with the necessary and fitting dispositions."

Brother Alonso Rodriguez was deeply wounded to know that his loved ones, helpless and aging women, should incur opposition to their holy practices at the end of their mortified lives. However, he counseled them to patience and constancy in the occasional letters he sent them. He bade them continue to receive Holy Communion just as they were doing, and pay no heed to the tongues of detractors.

Alonso was pleased to know that the first Jesuit whom he had known, and who became his confessor in Segovia, Father Santander, now an old man, had returned from Valencia to the former city, and was now the spiritual guide of Antonia and Juliana Rodriguez. The most recent epistle received from the two women told of the influence of this holy religious upon them, as well as of their burden of trial:

"Since the arrival of Father Santander," they wrote, "the great persecution we have been suffering because of our frequent Communions has greatly abated. Some persons, who could not understand our way of life, went to our confessor, to try to persuade him to forbid us to go so often to Communion, and they said such unkind things about us that if our Lord had not protected us with His almighty hand, we should have got into great trouble.

"Still, we did not complain, and, as we tried to conform ourselves to God's Will, He moved the heart of our confessor to continue his permission for Holy Communion. We are resolved to do nothing but what we are told to do, since we are sure that the order comes from God; and we obey it with great joy, because we know perfectly well that we ought to do God's will in all things."

This pathetic appeal for sympathetic understanding and advice evoked a prompt and full response from Brother Alonso Rodriguez. He recognized the fact that his sisters, living cloistered lives, yet not in the cloister, did not enjoy the favor of religious women in that day. The straitened financial circumstances of their family at the time when they were prepared to choose a state in life did not permit them to provide the necessary dowry which would have admitted them to the cloister. Their lives were more exposed to the shafts of the world than were those of their more sheltered sisters in religion, for they remained in the world, yet apart from it.

Alonso congratulated them on the cheerfulness and courage with which they had borne and surmounted their difficulties and sufferings. He encouraged them to persevere on the royal path of sacrifice, and promised them the continued help of his prayers and penances for their success.

He learned, with sorrow, that at this time one or other of the two women was usually ill. Added to this, Juliana suffered from scruples, and, as she had told Alonso of this, he could advise her about overcoming them. She felt that his counsel was as valuable as that of the most distinguished theologian, although she did not know that her saintly brother had experienced a similar trial.

As the health of Antonia, the younger of the sisters, steadily declined, she began to suffer continual pain. Alonso instructed her on the manner of bearing this, "for the love of God."

Before long, his anxiety for this beloved soul gave way to prayers for her eternal repose, for Antonia died on July 7, 1614, after a few days' illness.

The funeral services for the sister of one whom all believed was a saint were conducted as though Antonia had been a noblewoman of Segovia. The most illustrious citizens of the town carried her light coffin on their shoulders to the Jesuit Church, where a large congregation, including many of the first personages of Segovia, were assembled.

In accordance with the old Spanish custom, Antonia was laid before the altar, dressed in semi-religious garb. At the conclusion of the solemn rites, she was borne into the chapel of the Virgin, beside the main altar, and there interred.

Juliana Rodriguez had asked as a favor from God that she might soon follow her beloved sister into eternity. She was so certain that her prayer would be granted that she began to prepare for the end. Her days were spent at the foot of her crucifix, and her prayers and austerities were continued, as far as her confessor would permit.

One month and a half passed in this manner, and God answered Juliana's prayer. She passed peacefully from earth, the last Rodriguez to leave the yellow house in the Plaza del Azoquejo, and was buried with the same dignified and solemn rites as those which had accompanied her sister to the tomb.

Alonso was satisfied to place his dear ones in the keeping of Him who had called them to high perfection for His sake, and to remember them faithfully, so long as he lived. With the last tie broken in Segovia, he turned with renewed confidence and love to his holy vocation and tried to prove more and more worthy of the great favors he had received.

As he daily witnessed the evidences of distinguished virtue in the lives of his companions at our Lady's Mount, he realized more fully the greatness of the man who had laid the foundation for such achievement. The Blessed Ignatius Loyola had furnished the pattern for his militant sons. Through the strong bulwark of the rules and constitutions of the Society of Jesus he had provided for their every need on the way to sanctified labors here and unending glory hereafter.

Without translating his feelings into thoughts, Alonso realized how truly elevated his holy founder was in every thought, word, deed, and aspiration of his marvelous life. The mind of Ignatius was "a mind sure, vast, profound, comprehensive, fitted for speculation or action. His judgment was clear and solid. With sure vision he read the hearts of men and detected accurately the twistings and turnings of the mind. He possessed a marvelous discretion in treating with all characters, classes, and conditions. Mature deliberation, firmness of resolve, skill in counsel, compelling persuasion, vigorous execution, were his.

He showed courage in facing difficult undertakings and perseverance in carrying them through; constancy in supporting adversity and resourcefulness in surmounting obstacles. He was ready at all points, grasped all details, knew when to give way and when to insist, to yield or hold fast as circumstances indicated; to show severity or mildness, condescension or determination as the case required."

Brother Alonso Rodriguez believed that he alone, of all the Jesuits at Montesion, failed to reach the standard of this giant of God, Ignatius of Loyola. He felt that he could never do enough to atone for his faults and negligences.

Father Julian, who succeeded Father Gil as rector of the college, did not feel that way about Brother Rodriguez. As soon as he entered the house, he looked for him and planned to meet him, privately. When he learned that Alonso was confined to bed with a fever, he went immediately to the sick room.

When he had spoken with Alonso for more than an hour on spiritual topics, he asked: "Does your head ache, Brother?"

The truthful Alonso replied: "Yes, Father."

"Then don't talk any more, Brother," the rector said.

All through the rest of the day, and that evening, Brother Carrio wondered why his patient remained silent, saying nothing even when asked a question. The Infirmarian thought he should tell Father Julian about this unwonted silence, since the new rector did not have much knowledge of Alonso's habits.

The following morning, in response to Brother Carrio's call, Father Julian came into Alonso's room. When he entered, the sick man said to him:

"With your permission, Father, I will answer the Brother Infirmarian and the doctor, when they ask me how I am."

"Of course, Brother Rodriguez. But why did you think you could not answer without telling me?"

"Because, Father, you told me, yesterday, not to talk any more."

"I understand, Brother," Father Julian said, exchanging a significant glance with the Infirmarian. "But now you may talk all you wish."

The Brother Infirmarian had another patient in the house at this time. Brother Antony Puigdorfila, who had returned to Montesion upon the completion of most of his philosophy course, was seriously ill. He had asked his confessor, after receiving Extreme Unction and the Holy Viaticum, if he could send a message to Brother Rodriguez, without indulging self-love. Brother Puigdorfila was troubled by scruples, and he believed Alonso could help him.

The priest replied that he could do so, provided that he acted in submission to God's will.

The scholastic sent his message to Alonso, asking his prayers that he might be relieved of his trouble, if God wished.

As soon as Alonso received the message, he offered prayers for his beloved young friend's deliverance from the scruples. Brother Puigdorfila's difficulty left him, and he felt at peace, and confident that he would not be troubled again.

One of the students at Montesion over whom Brother Rodriguez exercised a strong influence for good was Diego Saura. Although he was only sixteen years of age, Diego seized every chance to speak with the aged Brother, and ask his prayers. Diego was distressed about his standing in his studies, and he worried as to whether he would pass his tests. One day he requested Brother Carrio to take a message for him to Alonso. The message was a request for prayers to assist Diego in his studies.

Brother Carrio carried the message. When Alonso had heard it, he told the Infirmarian: "Say to that student that he should not trouble himself about anything; that I charge myself with his difficulties, and that I shall not forget to pray for him. Tell him that if he wishes to do the will of God, he must become a religious."

Diego Saura was thrilled to hear this counsel from the famous

Brother. He begged that he might visit him, and when he was told he could do so, he went at once. At Alonso's bedside, he thanked him for his interest and help, and promised to follow the advice.

Alonso replied that God was calling the young man to the Company of Jesus, and that he ought to seek admission without delay.

The student did so. Soon afterward he brought another young man to visit Alonso, so that he, also, could receive counsel. Alonso told the two students: "Be most devout to our Lady, and especially to her Immaculate Conception. You must recite in its honor the Hail Mary and the Hail Holy Queen twelve times each day, asking her to intercede with her most holy Son that, as she was pure and free from original sin and every fault, she may keep you pure and spotless, so that hereafter you may see and enjoy her and her Blessed Son in heaven.

"In all your trials, fly at once to our Lady, like a little child which cries, as it turns to its mother: 'Mother! Mother!' "

The two students were delighted to be privileged to receive this personal counsel from the venerable Brother.

Everyone in the house at Montesion realized that their Brother Rodriguez was slipping away from them, little by little. They were anxious to keep in close touch with him at all times, in order to study his great virtues and obtain his help in their necessities. The scraps of the new habit which the late Father Jose de Villegas had ordered the Brother Tailor to cut down were by this time divided into infinitesimal shreds, as, one after another, the scholastics and lay brothers begged a relic from a companion who had picked up a piece from the floor.

North of the Church of Montesion the Calle del Sol, Street of the Sun, led upward into the Plaza of the Temple. When Fathers and Brothers were returning to the college over this street, after finishing some business in the city, they walked more quickly, fearful lest their idolized Brother Rodriguez might not be there when they arrived.

And when Brother Carrio, passing along the corridors, or little Brother Mora, at the door, saw the beacon flares come up along the island shore, they thought with a sense of deep loss of the time when some dawn would see the light of their saintly Brother's life quenched in this world, to shine again in an endless day.

One of the favorite devotions of Brother Alonso Rodriguez was the Little Office of our Lady. He was very eager to make it known and loved by the scholastics and lay brothers, as well as the students at Montesion. In one of her instructions to him, the Immaculate Virgin had told him to use it himself, and encourage others to use it.

In his diffidence and distrust of his own merits, he would gladly have left this task to the Fathers of the community. But the august Virgin had directed him to make copies of the Office and distribute them to those about him.

Brother Antony Mora, who often visited Alonso, told Father Julian, the rector, that Brother Rodriguez was doing a great deal of writing, and he asked the rector what he thought was the subject of it. Father Julian did not know, but he told Brother Mora to try, in a casual manner, to find out.

Antony did so. He returned to the rector with the word that: "Brother Rodriguez is composing a Little Office of the Blessed Virgin."

"Brother, take care not to tell that to anyone else," was Father Julian's rejoinder. "If Brother Rodriguez is writing the Little Office, he is copying it from a little book which he has in his possession. I must confess I am curious to know what started him doing this. Perhaps we shall soon find out."

When the rector questioned Alonso about the matter, Alonso told him that the Holy Virgin had set him to the work, and that he hoped to accomplish a great deal, in order to satisfy her. He was copying the Office from his little book.

Brother Mora, however, had not clearly understood what the rector said to him about the writing. After the beloved lay

Brother had passed away, he deposed before the ecclesiastical authorites that the Little Office of our Lady was the composition of the venerable religious. Actually, it had existed long before Alonso's time, originating in Spain.

Through his zeal, exercised in copying the Little Office, Alonso caused the devotion to spread throughout many lands. At this very time, 1615, it received the approval of Pope Paul V, who attached an indulgence for the recitation of the antiphon and prayer at its end.

The Blessed Virgin had long been venerated throughout Majorca under the title of the Immaculate Conception. The glorious prerogative had not as yet been defined as a dogma of the Church, and some theologians disputed it. Among those who espoused it warmly were the Fathers at Montesion.

During the time of the reigning Pontiff, Paul V, a strong controversy was raging over the question of grace as a mystery of faith.

Now, in November, 1615, the Franciscan and Jesuit faculties of Palma had defined the regular thesis on the question: How should we reconcile man's liberty with the divine prescience and the economy of grace?

A third group of religious, of another Order, held opposing views, as did certain others. They wrote out a thesis, in which they cast doubt on the doctrine of the Immaculate Conception, and posted a copy of it on the city walls.

The authorities of Palma were disturbed over this. They met in council and discussed the means to be adopted in removing the cause of the trouble, and at the same time arouse the popular interest by splendid festivities in honor of the Immaculate Conception. They dispatched a deputation to the viceroy, Don Carlos Coloma, also to the rector of Montesion, Father Julian, asking them to aid in the preparations for the fiesta.

The viceroy was distressed by the fact that an offensive thesis had been posted on the walls of the city. He sent for the superiors who were responsible for it, and told them that if they did not remove it, he would enforce an ancient royal decree by which all who opposed the doctrine of the Immaculate Conception could be expelled from Majorca.

For a time the authors of the thesis held out against this verdict. But on the day following its posting, a great throng of citizens marched to the walls and painted the placards over with the crosses used in the examination of heretics.

The authors of the thesis believed that they had caused sufficient trouble, and they canceled their crusade, removing the placards. So all was quiet once more.

The festivities in honor of the Immaculate Virgin were initiated with a great street procession of the ecclesiastical and civil authorities, a fireworks display, and sacred and allegorical masques and mystery plays.

During this memorable celebration, Brother Alonso Rodriguez had shared in the honors paid to our Lady with all the fervor and simplicity of his childlike heart. And he had also furnished all the community with an exhibition all his own, a type of fireworks which they had never known he was capable of setting off.

It happened at dinner on one of the days of the octave. Alonso had heard about the offending thesis which cast doubt on our Lady's great prerogative, and it had touched him deeply.

The thesis was being discussed at dinner, and Father Julian was watching Alonso closely, to observe the effect of the talk upon him.

Although always very gentle and unobtrusive, as he heard what had been done in the matter of the placards, he rose from his seat, standing without support, although he was very infirm and tottered in his walk.

He raised both arms to heaven, and in a voice trembling with emotion, cried out:

"You cannot trifle with the Mother of God, who, although she is so gentle, even sweetness and kindness itself, has a Son who is very jealous of His Mother's honor, and angels without number, who would take the part of their Lady and defend her purity and high name."

Fathers and Brothers were astonished at this display of fervor. No one moved or spoke, but all waited to hear what Brother Rodriguez had further to say to them.

He continued: "One of the causes, among others, why God sent the Company into this world was chiefly this: to teach and defend the truth in our Holy Mother Church."

One of the Fathers asked him: "Brother Rodriguez, how do you know that God sent the Society to defend the doctrine of the Immaculate Conception of our Lady?"

"I am certain of it!" was the burning reply. Then, again lifting his arms and eyes to heaven, he added: "From there! From on high. They have told me. And if Father Rector will give me permission, I will go and preach this in the streets of Palma."

"Thank you, Brother," the rector said, calmly. "We will remember what you have said."

Father Julian pondered a long time on this touching incident. Soon after the celebration in the city, he became ill. As he was confined to his room, he commissioned the young scholastic, Brother Colin, because this Brother was so close to Alonso, to go to him and ask him, in the name of his superior, how he knew what he had told the community at recreation a short time before.

The scholastic put the question, and Alonso replied:

"Brother Carisimo, I remember well what passed on that occasion. It is quite true that I said what you repeat. I had no vision, it is true, nor any external revelation of any kind on the matter. But there came to me a great impulse which I am certain was from heaven, that what I felt and said was a truth from on high. I still hold for certain it is as I said."

Alonso was consoled to know that the Blessed Ignatius Loyola had upheld and defended the doctrine of the Immaculate Conception, as had Fathers Francis Xavier, Laynez, and Borgia. The young novice, John Berchmans, had shared the veneration of our Lady under the title of Immaculate Conception, and had signed his name to his defense in his blood. Father Laynez had attributed the cure of many sick persons to her under that title, and, although very ill at the time, had eloquently spoken of it before the Council of Trent, winning an important concession in its favor.

The college barber had occasion to know how real was the spirit of mortification of Brother Alonso Rodriguez. He knew that Alonso waited for such service until he had to utilize the help of an inexperienced workman, a new hand. This man would twist and turn the head of his victim so ruthlessly that he often nicked his chin or face. When this pseudo barber had finished his torture, the Brother would rise from the chair, make a profound bow to his tormentor, and walk off. Brother Antony Mora had occasion to witness this performance, and he wondered whether he should not tell Father Julian about it, for fear Brother Rodriguez might be killed before it was time for him to die. Knowing how Alonso loved to be inconvenienced and ill-treated, he did not mention it to the rector.

Brother Colin, the scholastic who was so dear to Brother Alonso Rodriguez, had received orders to go to Spain. He was to set out from Montesion in October, 1616. As the time of his departure drew near, the thought of parting with his revered friend made him very heavy at heart.

One Saturday evening he visited Alonso's room, and spent some time talking with him. Then Alonso gave the young religious his blessing, and bade him depart.

Afterward, Brother Colin told Father Julian of the meeting:

"I found Brother Rodriguez sitting on the boards which support his mattress. But he was so absorbed in God that I knelt at his feet and kissed them before he knew I had entered the room. When he saw me there, as I was about to rise, he was much distressed, for he did not want any such attention.

"I asked him to give me some last counsel as a remembrance of the time we had spent together here at Montesion.

"He told me that when I wanted to obtain anything from God, I should beg it from our Lady with confidence. 'Be very devout to her, and all will go well with you,' he said. Those were his last words to me, Father."

Father Julian consoled the scholastic as best he could, but he felt as if he also needed some consolation. Brother Alonso Rodriguez became dearer to those about him, as they realized that his beautiful life was nearing its close.

Brother Antony Mora, who had exchanged his post of Infirmarian for that of porter, was highly elated when he was told that he might share some of the work of the present Infirmarian, Brother Carrio. Antony was very careful to see that Alonzo was not left alone for long at a time, and he profited by this close association to learn more still about the holy soul of Brother Rodriguez.

Alonso liked to have his young friend read to him from a book entitled *Religious Perfection,* the work of a Jesuit, Father Luke Penelli. It was a treatise on patience, directed in a particular way to those in affliction. Originally an Italian work, it had been translated into Spanish, and was very popular at the time.

Alonso never tired of hearing certain passages read from this book. He also wished to look often on a little print of our Lady, which he kept close at hand, saying that it gave him great courage to bear his sufferings.

About six months before his death, Alonso suffered an almost complete loss of memory. This was the most severe of all his trials, for it deprived him of the comfort of reciting his usual prayers. He could scarcely remember the Our Father and Hail Mary. Brother Mora would recite them for him, slowly, and in a clear loud voice, trying to refresh the memory of his dear friend.

When Father Julian saw the young Lay Brother so devoted and assiduous at the side of the aged Alonso, he thought that heaven must be very much pleased with Antony. For he could have been out in Majorca, enjoying the pleasures of life given even to the lowliest youth in that lovely country. Whereas, here he was, content to devote himself, hiddenly, and unknown to the outer world, in the arduous duties of his charges, the door, and the Infirmary.

Father Torrens, who was Alonso's spiritual director, sometimes wrote down what the sick Brother told him in regard to what went on in his conscience. Alonso could no longer hold a pen to write, and Father Julian was very anxious to secure as much knowledge as possible about him while he still lived.

Those of the Community who, on one pretext or other, had succeeded in obtaining Alonso's signature or some written bits of his counsels, knew that they had been very fortunate, because now their beloved Brother Rodriguez could write no more.

Father Julian had also tried to accumulate as many souvenirs of Alonso as possible, to be divided among the Jesuit houses, later on. He was happy to grant the requests which came from some high officials of Palma, for portraits of the holy Brother. Some drawings had been made of his profile when he did not suspect that he was the object of so much veneration. At the urgent plea of the Duchess of Gandia, the rector forwarded one of these drawings and a letter written by Alonso, also a rosary for her son, to the pious woman. That son was Cardinal Gaspar de Brija Velasco, Bishop of Albano, and Spanish Ambassador to Rome. The Cardinal was the grandson of the late Father General of the Society, Father Francis Borgia.

Among the nobles of Palma who felt most keenly the anticipated loss of Brother Rodriguez was Don Carlos de Coloma, who had held numerous important offices in the city.

Other notables of the Island who honored the humble Brother were Don Ildefonso Lasso Sedano, who was bishop of Majorca for about three years, and who died there in 1617; Father Creus, of the Order of Saint Dominic, the Inquisitor, a man of very austere life, and Father Rafael Serra, who had three times served as Provincial of the Franciscans.

Father Serra never tired of saying that he owed much to the prayers of the wonder-working Brother. In speaking with Alonso one day, Father Serra had asked him:

"Tell me, Brother, if our Lord said to you that if you wished to go to heaven, you might go there at once, or if you wished to stay in this world, you might do that—which would you choose?"

Alonso had replied:

"I would choose to do the will of God."

"But, Brother," insisted Father Serra, "if God left the matter with you, and He desired you to choose and do what you liked best, what would you do?"

"I never want to do anything except God's will, and that alone I would choose to do. I prefer it to heaven itself, because I would rather give pleasure to God than possess eternal happiness, if it could be obtained without God's will."

Father Serra proposed no further questions. But he had remarked to a member of the community at Montesion:

"Your Order has in this Brother another Giles."

XVII

EARLY in February Alonso noticed that his faithful friend and spiritual guide, Father Torrens, had not visited his sick chamber for some time, and that Brother Antony Mora was unusually preoccupied and seemingly anxious about something.

"What has happened to Father Torrens?" he finally asked Antony.

Brother Mora knew that it would be useless to conceal the fact that Father Torrens was very ill. So he told Alonso. A little later, after visiting Father Torrens, Antony said to the venerable Brother: "Father Torrens begs you to commend him to God, for he is seriously ill. The doctor says that if his present symptoms continue, he will have to bleed him. He was on the point of doing so tonight, for Father's fever was very high and his head ached badly. Pray to our Lord for him, Brother."

Father Torrens' fever and headache was not helped by his anxiety over his assignment as preacher of the Lenten course given on Sunday evenings at Montesion. He had carefully prepared his discourses, but now he felt that he must request the rector to find a substitute. The doctor had told him that he would be obliged to stay in bed at least until Easter, so that any outside activity was not possible.

At ten o'clock in the evening the Brother Infirmarian for the time being, Brother Mora, came into Alonso's room and told him about Father Torrens' anxiety. "Pray, Brother," he said.

Alonso began to pray for his beloved spiritual father, and Brother Mora went back to the room of the sick priest. But he remained absent only a few minutes. Then he returned to Alonso.

"Father Torrens has just fallen into a quiet sleep," he announced, jubilantly. "It is the first sleep of the kind he has had for days. But, pray on, Brother Rodriguez. We want to have him up for the Lenten course."

Father Torrens enjoyed a peaceful night. When the doctor arrived in the morning, prepared to apply the leeches for the bleeding, he was much surprised to find that his patient was greatly improved, so that the operation was not necessary. But he told the priest to remain in bed that day, because he was afraid he might take a cold and suffer a relapse, if he rose too soon.

As soon as the doctor had left the premises, Father Torrens got up, dressed, and went into the domestic chapel and celebrated Mass. He suffered no ill effects whatever from doing so. He continued well, and several days later, began the Lenten course of sermons, as arranged. He preached during the Solemn Exposition of the most Blessed Sacrament, and also heard many confessions. When Father Julian inquired how he felt, he replied: "It is many years, Father Rector, since I have felt so well, and for such a long period of time. I owe it all to Brother Rodriguez' prayers."

Five months went by, and Alonso remained in his little room. Up to the end of this period, he had not regained his memory. But now he discovered, to his great joy, that it was restored. He discovered this one morning, immediately after receiving Holy Communion.

Although often feverish, nothing was permitted to interfere with Alonso's reception of his Blessed Lord in Holy Communion three times weekly. In April he had lost the use of his body from the waist down. However, he could move his legs a little, also his arms.

Brother Antony Mora was very proud to be entrusted once more with the care of the dear invalid. He insisted that Alonso should lie quietly in the narrow bed and not try to lift himself when he was about to receive Communion. But it seemed that he could always manage to pay this respect to his Sacramental Lord.

Sometimes Brother Mora, coming softly in at the door, would hear his patient praying aloud:

"More sufferings, O Lord! A great deal more! But more charity and patience with them!" It was the cry of the Blessed Ignatius Loyola, his illustrious founder, and of Father Francis Xavier, his favorite disciple and follower. It was the cry of many other valiant soldiers of the Company of Jesus, as they found themselves called upon to pass the acid test of physical suffering and infirmity.

May came, and Father Julian was to have his turn in bearing the cross of ill-health. He was attacked by a severe case of gout, and his physician, Doctor Santendreu, considered his condition very alarming. He believed that, at best, a month would elapse before the Father Rector could hope for improvement.

The two lay brothers, Brothers Carrio and Mora, were carrying Alonso from his room to the lower tribune, so that he might hear Mass. The path led past the rector's door. When they reached it, Alonso pleaded to be allowed to see Father Julian.

The Brothers granted his wish. Father Julian was very much pleased to have the unexpected visit. He said to Alonso:

"You know, Brother, I have a great devotion to the Immaculate Conception. So, I want you to obtain, through our Lady, for the sake of her glorious privilege, that I may be cured."

Alonso promised that he would do his best to obtain the favor. When he had heard Mass and was again tucked away in bed, he began at once to importune the Blessed Virgin to cure the sick priest. He spent the entire day doing this.

He was still praying earnestly when the shadows began to steal from the mauve tops of the mountains across the quiet bay and through the windows of the room.

All in an instant, a pale light glowed above Alonso's bed. As he gazed upward, the lovely Lady of his desire stood there, as she had stood beside him on several previous occasions. Once more she spoke to him:

"You have nothing to fear, Alonso. I will take the matter into my own hands."

His heart filled with heavenly consolation, Alonso stopped praying for Father Julian. Instead, he began to thank God and the august Virgin for this new and wonderful manifestation.

In the morning Father Julian awoke as usual. But, instead of feeling the excruciating pain he had suffered in his legs, he felt none at all. Every symptom of his disease had disappeared, at least for the time being. All the community knew that these attacks generally lasted for several weeks at a time, sometimes for two months. They were astonished at the change in his condition, as was the doctor. Although they had often experienced the fruits of Brother Alonso Rodriguez' zeal and charity and his power with God, they always feared that these favors might not continue.

Father Julian was to continue for an entire year quite free from his old trouble. Now, since he was well, he took his turn in visiting his saintly friend. He thanked Alonso for his holy prayers and solicitude, and he noticed, with pain in his heart, that the Brother had drooped even since he had last seen him.

On the seventeenth day of August, Father Torrens took down the final manifestation of conscience of Brother Alonso Rodriguez. When all the community were together, he read it to them, with tears in his eyes. He told them:

"Brother Rodriguez said to me that the moment he communicated and began his thanksgiving, he fancied himself in heaven, in the presence of the Holy Trinity, surrounded by multitudes of angels and archangels, and saints, in a marvelous glory. Meanwhile, he was expressing his gratitude to God for His infinite graces, because, although Lord of such splendor and majesty, He deigned to come to visit so vile a creature. He asked favors for himself and for those who had commended themselves to him, and our Lord deigned to hear him.

"Brother Rodriguez also told me that in the past, nearly every day, morning and evening, he fell into a rapture. Once, in particular, after receiving Holy Communion on the feast of our Lady's Assumption, the Blessed Virgin took him in her arms and presented him to the eternal Father and to the Blessed Trinity. Our Lady had on one side Brother Rodriguez' Guardian Angel, and on the other his name saint, St. Ildefonso. He especially remarked that he recognized all these saints and angels just as if he had been with them all his life, and he saw each one of them as clearly as if he had been looking at one, only."

Father Torrens remarked that this vision was similar to one which had been granted to Alonso once, in a church in Segovia. He had never forgotten it. Now, near the end of a long lifetime, he had told Father Torrens about it.

November, Month of the Holy Souls, came, and with it intensified suffrages for the Fathers and Brothers of Montesion who had gone from earth, and whose mortal remains were enshrined in the Lady Chapel of the college church.

Father Torrens believed that the time had come to prepare

Brother Rodriguez for his journey into eternity by giving him the Last Sacraments of the Church.

When he was told this, Alonso was very happy. Although death did not seem imminent, Father Marimon, his confessor, heard his confession, then anointed him and gave him the Holy Viaticum. Alonso answered the beautiful prayers as calmly and clearly as if they were being said for another.

He received Holy Communion a few times after this. Each time he asked the Brother Infirmarian to lift him, in reverence to his Lord. He could use his arm slightly, and he removed the little cap he wore on the crown of his head for this visit. He remained alone, making his thanksgiving for some time after each Communion.

The lively young Antony entertained a certain curiosity as to whether Alonso knew the exact time of his death. He thought it probable that he did, but, also, that no answer would be forthcoming if he should ask the question outright. So he adopted a ruse, in his effort to find out.

He read to Alonso several chapters from the life of a holy nun, Blessed Caterina Tomas, formerly an Augustinian of the Convent of Santa Maria Magdalena, at Palma. The Sister had passed away several years before this time, in the reputation of sanctity. The time of her death had been revealed to her, and she asked for the Last Sacraments before her physician thought it necessary they should be administered. However, she received them, and died soon after, on the very day she had foretold, which was Holy Thursday.

Brother Mora selected certain passages bearing on the subject in which he was interested. Then he laid down the book, and asked Alonso:

"Brother, this holy nun foretold the day and hour of her death some time before she passed away. How is it that you don't tell me when you are to die, although I am sure you know?"

The reply was: "That is a subject in which little is to be gained, and many a snare met with."

Antony was greatly disappointed. However, he tried again. This time Alonso answered:

"Brother, this is a temptation. Man's life is in the hands of God, and He will send death when He chooses. May it please His divine majesty that I shall be ready when it comes. We should be on the lookout, and always prepared when our Lord calls us. This is true happiness.

"What good will it do me to know or say when I am to die? To suffer, and to suffer much, for God's love, this is worth our while, and of first importance. We shall die when God wills; and Christ says: 'Blessed is that servant whom his Master shall find watching when he shall come from the feast and nuptials of heaven.'"

For a time Brother Mora ceased questioning his patient. But a short time afterward, by skillful cross-questioning when Alonso was not on guard, he managed to ascertain that his patient would die one week from that time.

Antony managed to win this knowledge by telling Alonso:

"Brother, Father Minister is anxious to be present with you at the end. But he does not know whether he will have time to finish his retreat at our country house, where Father Julian wishes him to go for that purpose, in time to return here to assist you."

Alonso replied: "It will be well if Father Minister does not go away." When he learned that the Father had not gone, he remarked to Antony:

"Father Minister has acted well. I thank him for his kindness, because he will pray for me to our Lord, and, by staying here, will be present at my death."

All his mental trials had passed from the venerable Brother as death approached. He told Father Torrens that this had happened after Holy Communion, on Saturday, the twenty-eighth day of the month. Even his bodily pains ceased, although he took little food and he appeared to have lost his hearing, since he made no reply to the questions put to him.

His face remained very bright and serene, and when any member of the community entered the room, he recognized him and smiled.

At midnight on the last day of our Lady's month of the Rosary the final trial came to the aged Brother. He began to suffer such great pains in every part of his thin frame that again and again he murmured in agony: "Jesus! Jesus! O, Jesus! My Jesus!"

Father Julian and the other members of the community were notified by Brother Mora that Brother Rodriguez was near death. One and all came quickly to the little room. Those who could not gain admittance to it, because it was so small, knelt outside in the corridor, looking through the open door.

Alonso's heart action and his pulse were very weak and feeble. Those closest to the bed touched their rosaries and other pious objects to his hands. For half an hour they continued to do this, for themselves and for those who handed such objects to them, to be laid on the dying Brother. Meanwhile, the litanies for the dying and other prayers of the Church were recited.

For half an hour the beautiful spirit of Brother Alonso Rodriguez lingered in the little chamber where he had spent nearly forty-six years of his religious life.

At last, his head sank a little, the hands ceased to make the effort to bless those about him, and all saw that the end had come.

Father Julian began the recommendation of a departing soul, while Brother Alonso Rodriguez opened his eyes very wide and fixed them with a look of ineffable love upon his brothers in the community. They had never seen him appear so bright, for he had been a self-effacing religious, who never spoke of the wealth of affection for his own which had filled his holy heart.

Then he lowered his eyes to the crucifix in his thin hands, and kissed its feet devoutly.

With a strong cry, he spoke the Holy Name: "Jesus!"

Then Brother Alonso Rodriguez was gone from Montesion,

from those who had loved and reverenced him, to be their model and intercessor before the throne of God.

It was shortly after midnight when the community, with the exception of Fathers Julian and Torrens, the Infirmarian and a few others, filed away from the scene of death.

Then Father Torrens, who had known more of the soul of the dead Brother than any other, gently folded the tired hands, closed the eyes, and prepared Brother Rodriguez for his bier.

As he rested, like a serene spirit, on the hard bed, those about him strove to fix in their minds the last impression of their Brother, as he had been on this earth.

His body was of medium stature, but infirmity had caused him to appear shorter than he actually was. He was very thin. His face was oval in shape, the forehead high, with a little fringe of snow white hair encircling a bald crown. His eyes, now closed in death, had long been sunken and dimmed by the vigils he had kept and the tears he had shed over what he believed were his great faults. The nose, slender and straight, was a little pinched from long sickness. The mouth was small. The hands were very thin, with veins and bones showing through the blue-white skin.

The emaciated body was reverently clothed in the habit and cloak the Brother had worn in life, and laid upon its bier in the chamber. The few articles Alonso had used, with the exception of the bed, were removed from the room. Jealously, Brother Antony Mora took away the "little sprig of green" which had remained close to the aged saint in his final hour.

Then one of the brothers went to ring the community bell, to tell the city of the passing of one of their number.

When she heard the voice of the bell, a lady who lived near the college hurried to the window overlooking Montesion. As she looked toward the residence, she saw a light glowing over it, although dawn had not yet broken in the east. She called one of her servants, who also saw the light. It remained for some time above the house, then slowly faded away.

The bell aroused all Palma. Nobles and city officials soon arrived at the residence. The Royal Procurator and the members of the Royal Council were in the group. All seemed to know that it was Brother Rodriguez who had departed.

Soon others came, Judges, the Canons of the Cathedral, religious superiors of other Orders, and the humbler townsfolk.

Hundreds of men surged in and out of the house, from the time they had arisen, at the sound of the bell, until morning broke. Most of those who came placed rosaries, handkerchiefs and other tokens on the remains of the dead Brother. Not only the little chamber, and the passage leading to it, but the cloister of the quadrangle of the college and the porteria, where Brother Rodriguez had served so many years, were filled with people.

Meanwhile, in the church, where the departed religious had so often served Mass and knelt in prayer, members of his community were getting ready for his last triumph.

Brother Alonso Rodriguez, formed Coadjutor of the Society of Jesus, of the Community of Montesion, Palma, Majorca, had merited these honors. In his long years in religious life he had illustrated all that the Blessed Ignatius Loyola had wished for his spiritual sons, when he wrote into the Rules for the lay Brothers, humble servitors of the servants of Christ:

"They ought to perform the offices entrusted to their charge as exactly as they can, with all humility and charity. By this they will not only purchase the full reward of their labors and sweat, but will share also in all the good works which God vouchsafes to work through the whole Company, for His service and praise."

XVIII

A STRANGE unwonted quiet brooded over Palma by the sea.

The bells of mourning had ceased to toll for the passing

of Brother Alonso Rodriguez. Now the pale light of another dawn crept up in the east, revealing the rambling houses at the water's edge, like old men, solitary and forgotten, the cactus and prickly pear clinging to their walls like hoary beards.

At sun-up signs of life began to show in the town. Mule-drawn carts lumbered through the Moorish arch in the walls and over the drawbridge into the open country. Sleepy-eyed servants appeared in courtyards, water jugs or market baskets on their heads. Priests, dressed in black vestments, approached the altars, to offer the Holy Sacrifice of the Mass for the repose of Brother Alonso Rodriguez, but feeling that it would be more fitting to offer it in his honor. In the palace and in the cottage of the peasant a somber silence prevailed. There were many who felt the cross of separation from one who had counseled and comforted and healed them, in soul and body alike.

So the morning of the Feast of All Saints passed.

At one o'clock, immediately after the noon repast at Montesion, loving hands carried the body of the dead Brother from the college to the church.

Because great throngs were waiting to pay homage to the dead, and the courtyard, as well as the adjoining streets were jammed with people, the Fathers of the college had decided to have a platform erected outside the sanctuary of the church as a place of repose for the remains. This platform was six feet high, and covered with black cloth.

Although their burden was very light, it was difficult for the scholastics and lay brothers, who carried the bier, to bear Brother Rodriguez to his place of honor before the altar. The passage through which they must walk was choked with people, young and old, rich and poor, learned and unlettered, who had come to pay their respects to one whom all esteemed as a saint and wonder-worker.

Father Marimon, who had been Alonso's ordinary confessor most of the time during the last fifteen years of the Brother's life, was one of the Jesuits in charge of the arrangements. His heart was crushed with sorrow by this death. He had first met Brother Rodriguez in 1575, when he had enrolled in the student body at Montesion, a boy of fifteen. Received into the Company of Jesus in 1580, he had come in 1601 to Montesion to become a member of the teaching faculty. There he had become more intimately acquainted with Brother Rodriguez.

Father Julian had commissioned Father Marimon to write down the entire proceedings following the death of Alonso until after his burial. The rector wished to send the account to the Father General at Rome, and he believed that no one was better qualified to do this than the young priest. Father Julian himself set to work to compose a short circular letter, to be sent to all the houses of the Society in the Aragon Province, as a death notice.

In the moments between his pressing duties in the church, Father Marimon sat down at the desk Brother Rodriguez had used so long, and with misty eyes and trembling hand, wrote the account, beginning with the transfer of the precious remains from the residence to the church:

"We formed in procession behind the bier and reverently and in deep sorrow followed it.

"When the inside of the church was gained, the noise of the concourse of people was so great that it was impossible to continue the chant. So great was the rush of people, principally noble ladies of Palma, to see the Brother, that the procession was completely disintegrated. It was necessary for Fathers and Brothers to put shoulder to shoulder around the body and so, in serried ranks, proceed to the platform. The plan succeeded, but it was a slow process. . . ."

Because the catafalque was high, and four Fathers were posted, one at each corner, to guard the body and prevent anyone from ascending the steps, order was eventually restored. The crowd could now look upon the quiet face of the departed Brother, lighted up by wax candles, the gift of a citizen of Palma whom his prayers had restored to health.

Members of all the religious communities of Palma came to the church, to look for the last time on the loved countenance and form of one whom they esteemed as a great servant of God. They chanted the Divine Office at the bier, aged priests and young religious vying in honoring Brother Alonso Rodriguez. Many had known the dead religious when he held the post of porter at the college, and not a few owed their vocations to his holy influence. Some had been members of the student body at Montesion, and now returned to look upon their revered friend before he was carried to the tomb.

The cathedral chapter came to the church in procession with the diocesan clergy. By the order of the bishop, who was unable to be present, all chanted, to an organ accompaniment. It was believed that three hundred priests took part in the chant.

Many who came begged the Jesuits on guard at the bier to place objects of devotion on the sacred remains. They pleaded, also, for a bit of the worn cloak belonging to the dead Brother, and for the "measure of the holy body," a custom which prevailed at that time in all Catholic countries.

The four Jesuits on the platform soon found that they were unable to cope with this situation. At their request two Dominican Fathers ascended the steps and began to assist them in fulfilling the requests of the devout persons at the bier. Thousands of rosaries, medals and other religious articles were laid by the six priests on the hands of Brother Rodriguez. At the conclusion of this office, Father Marimon stated that at least eight thousand objects had been honored in this manner.

As if God wished to testify to His good pleasure in His faithful servant, a miraculous cure was wrought at the bier.

Among those who passed in the endless lines by the body was a mother with a young child in her arms. The little one had suffered for four months with inflammation of the eyes. No remedy had proved efficacious for their cure. Now this woman had come, with many others, to ask Brother Rodriguez to obtain the cure of her child's eyes.

Father Michael Redo listened to her plea, then, lifting the infant from her outstretched arms, applied its eyes to Brother Rodriguez' hands. He then passed the little one back, over the heads of the crowd, to its mother.

Instantly she cried out in a loud voice:

"See this child! My boy is cured! His eyes are well now! Thanks be to God!"

Meanwhile, the community of Montesion were seated in the sanctuary, singing the Matins for the Dead, although darkness was approaching. Just as they finished the chant, the bell rang, according to custom, for the sermon.

However, the magistrates of Palma approached Father Julian with a request. It was that the sermon might be postponed until the following day, Friday, November 3, the first free day after the solemnities of All Souls and All Saints Days.

Father Julian granted the request. But he and his councilors decided that it would not be possible to defer the burial of Brother Rodriguez under existing tropical conditions, and also because of the great throngs milling about in the church and city.

It was decided, in secret, to conduct the burial services after the church had been cleared of people. The body would then be placed in the vault prepared for it in the chapel of our Lady.

Five o'clock had come, and with it darkness.

Father Torrens, Alonso's long-time spiritual director, went into the pulpit and spoke to the people. He told them that the solemn services were to be held on the following day, and invited them to return then and assist at them. But he told them that Brother Rodriguez would be buried right then and there.

As soon as Father Torrens had left the pulpit, the entire community of Montesion, with many other religious and secular priests, entered the church in procession, by the door of the cloister. Hardly were they inside, however, when the procession was broken up by the pressure of the throng.

The Jesuits had intended to carry the body from its platform to the Lady chapel and inter it immediately, as Father Torrens had announced. But under existing circumstances, this plan was out of the question.

The clergy eventually made their way to the bier and sang the burial service about it. But the crowd pressed between them and the Lady chapel, making it impossible for them to remove the body.

A second time Father Torrens spoke to the throng. He told them that, since the night was closing in, the interment would not take place for the present. He encouraged them to return to their homes, and to come back on the morrow.

Taken somewhat off guard, little by little, they left the church and the Community were able to carry Brother Rodriguez from the platform back to the College.

Quite exhausted by their exertions of the day, they placed it in the first room they came to, Father Julian's. The doors of the house were then locked, so that no secular could gain entrance to it. Some people still remained in the church, but when nine o'clock came, all had departed.

Father Julian called his consultors and discussed the plan to be followed in the interment of Brother Rodriguez. They felt that it would be wise to bury him secretly, late that same night.

Since little time remained to them to pay their homage to their beloved confrere, all the community stayed close to him until the last. They placed many objects on the still body and prayed continuously for and to him, who had loved them so much and whom they had deeply loved in return.

It was found that the face and hands of Brother Rodriguez were quite soft, as in life, but that the skin of the forefinger and thumb of the right hand were callous, from his continual counting of his beads.

Some of the community cut off little fringes of his hair, others bits of his habit, the habit for which he had borne a stinging rebuke from the late Father Provincial Jose de Villegas. Others touched their beads and medals to his hands and face.

Father Marimon spent a few moments in continuing the account of the incidents of the past two days, according to the rector's orders:

"We placed the body of our Brother Alonso Rodriguez in a solid coffin of wood, and so we bade him adios, with confidence that we should see him, surrounded by great glory, in Heaven.

"We carried him in procession, but singing in a low tone, for fear we should be heard by those who were still waiting outside the church doors.

"We laid the body in the chapel prepared for it, the usual burying-place of ours. We went through all the ceremonies of our Holy Mother Church with tender devotion.

"The Feast of All Saints would soon commence. Doubtless it was so ordained that at that very time he had entered into the company of all the Saints.

"Our sovereign Lady, the most Blessed Virgin, gave him hospitality in her chapel of the Assumption, both because of the Brother's great devotion to that Mystery—and we know that he received signal favors on its beautiful Feast—and to assure us that the Queen of Heaven assisted at the entry of Brother Alonso Rodriguez into his glory, which he will enjoy with God, for all eternity."

The solemn funeral services were carried out on Friday morning in the college church, as had been arranged. About the catafalque, erected in the Lady chapel close to the tomb of the Brother, high dignitaries of the Church sang the Mass, assisted by members of the Jesuit community. At its conclusion, Father Torrens, who knew most about the secrets of the departed Brother, began the sermon, which lasted an hour and a half.

Gently lifting the veil which had shrouded the life of Brother Alonso Rodriguez from the world, and even from his companions in the religious life of the Company of Jesus, he revealed many of the heavenly favors granted to him, from the very first days of his novitiate.

When all was over, and the congregation had gone its various ways, the Fathers and Brothers of Montesion had their Brother Rodriguez to themselves for always, to bless their lives and to inspire them by the memory of his heroic example.

All the writings of the dead Brother were carefully collected with a view to his future beatification, for all believed that one day he would be elevated to the altars of the Church.

Among the papers found in his scant possessions was a sermon on his illustrious founder, Blessed Ignatius Loyola. At the end of the sermon, Alonso had written, with unsteady hand, as his infirmities grew more pronounced:

"And, just as God gave to His own people, after He had freed them, the manna of the wilderness, and sustained them by it, so He refreshed divinely, with the Manna of Heaven, those who had been freed by our Father Ignatius from the power of the heretics.

"And this Manna is God Himself. This Manna is that most exalted Food, the Blessed Sacrament, with which He will feed us until He leads us to the land of promise, which is Eternal Glory."

The stooping patient form of Brother Alonso Rodriguez would never again linger outside the door of his confessor's room, waiting, even hours, at the call of obedience, for the Jesuit to return. In the refectory, where Brother Rodriguez had practiced the most austere mortifications; at the Porteria, where he had gathered the little ones about him, to teach them the catechism while awaiting the summons of the bell; in the Infirmary, where he had preached his last discourse in the example of his fortitude and meekness, his gentle presence seemed to linger, as Fathers and Brothers prepared to take their well-earned repose for the night.

Like unbidden thoughts, shadows stole over the shining bay. Darkness settled over the city walls and the ancient buildings, and the night, in a robe of sable velvet, seemed to be making a meditation on Death.

Soon silence reigned in the rooms and corridors of Montesion, where, in his new-found tomb in the Chapel of his Lady, Brother Alonso Rodriguez enjoyed his first night's rest until the final Resurrection. In his life of noble sacrifice and loving compassion for others, he had fulfilled all the prophetic utterance of the saintly Provincial of the Society, Father Cordeses, who had admitted him, saying:

"I feel obliged to admit Alonso as a saint, for I am determined that he shall be one, and he will give great glory to the Company."

As the young moon rose over Palma, and the stars, jewels of the night, embroidered the sky, the walls and façades of Montesion stood bravely out, like the battlements of God, guarding their treasure of the living and the dead. The Company of Jesus had willed them to the world in the precious testament of their founder. Men who came and went at the sound of a bell, like sheep following their leader. Men who wore their clothing until often it was old and shabby; who went about with a few coins only in their pockets, or with nothing at all. Old men, wearied and broken after a life of selfless endeavor, after brilliant achievements for the greater glory of God, obeying young men, and young men obeying all. Men who rose very early in the morning the year round, dividing the long hours of the day between prayer and consecrated labors until at night they stretched their tired limbs on humble cots, to take the rest necessary to enable them to go on in another day. Men who had foresworn the comforts of home and family, the soft touch of gentle hands when their brows ached with pain, to labor and suffer. Men of the four grades established by Blessed Ignatius: Professed of the Four Vows, Professed of the Three Vows, Spiritual Coadjutors, Temporal Coadjutors. Teaching, preaching, administering the Sacraments, laboring in the lowliest offices of the house, as Brother Alonso Rodriguez had done, it was all the same, so that the lofty standard of personal holiness was reached, and souls won to Christ.

Already, at the death of Brother Rodriguez, the Company of Jesus had given its martyrs to the Church. Martyrs of Portuguese, Spanish, Japanese, English, Scotch nationalities, they had suffered the fate of those who defend Christ against the hatred of His enemies. Cast into the sea, drawn and quartered, hanged, burned at the stake, the sons of Saint Ignatius had justified his proud hopes of them. And those who knew the life and character of the departed Brother Rodriguez, believed that he, also, had suffered martyrdom, but bloodless, and that he was now enjoying the reward of his valor.

Young Brother Antony Mora, passing by the vacant room of Brother Alonso Rodriguez, and looking through a window at the island shores, saw that the beacon flares burned brightly.

But he knew that a great light had gone out from this world.

Epilogue

THE tomb of Brother Alonso Rodriguez in the chapel of our Lady at Montesion, Palma, became a shrine of pilgrimage from the very day of his death. One after another, miracles were wrought through his intercession, not alone in the island of Majorca and in Spain, but in Flanders, Italy, even in distant Mexico and Peru.

The report of these wonders caused Father Julian, the rector of Montesion, to ask that an official investigation should be opened and the life and works of the holy Brother carefully examined. The bishop of Majorca was pleased to grant the favor, and the investigation was begun, with a similar movement undertaken at Segovia, the birthplace and residence of Brother Rodriguez during the first four decades of his life.

The processes of Majorca and Segovia were officially submitted to the Sacred Congregation of Rites in 1622. Three years later, at the request of Philip IV, king of Spain, this Congregation declared that witnesses might be called and interrogated for the cause of canonization of Brother Rodriguez. However, numerous obstacles delayed the process until, in December of that year, Pope Urban VIII signed the commission for the introduction of the cause. By this act, Brother Alonso Rodriguez won the title of Venerable.

Anticipating their Brother Rodriguez' elevation to the altars, the Jesuits of Montesion began the erection of a magnificent chapel to which they expected, later, to transfer the holy body. But further delays in the cause ensued, and it was not until 1673 that an inquiry was instituted as to whether public veneration had been paid to the Brother. Some argument took place over this, but the objections were overruled, and Pope Innocent XI, in 1684, signed the order for a commission to resume the cause.

The *Memorial* which Brother Rodriguez had written at the command of his superiors was scrupulously examined by the ecclesiastical authorities. More delays followed the progress of the cause, however, and it was not until 1717 that Pope Clement XI solemnly approved the writings, declaring that nothing was to be found in them which would prevent the beatification of Brother Rodriguez. Processes followed one another after this until, in 1760, Pope Clement XIII published the decree declaring "that the virtues of the Venerable Alonso were proved to be of heroic degree."

The expulsion of the Jesuits from Spain and her possessions, and, in 1773, the suppression of the Society, again hindered the cause. The Jesuits of Montesion, however, returned to their former home when Pope Pius VII restored the Society to its former status, and the cause was again resumed. A second expulsion, in 1820, drove the religious from the college once more, to return in 1823. But this time their sorrows were mitigated when they learned that the two miracles proposed for the cause of Beatification of the Venerable Alonso Rodriguez had been approved by the Sacred Congregation of Rites. They also learned that His Holiness Pope Leo XII had solemnly published the approval of the Congregation's decree. The words of the Pontiff on the occasion would be forever memorable:

"We choose this day" (the Feast of the Founder of the Society of Jesus) "to show by new and marvelous proofs, that the holiness of the Order, founded by Saint Ignatius—and now reconstituted for the glory of God, the benefit of the Church, for the propagation and defense of the Church, for the education of Christian youth and the restoring of piety—is every day growing and increasing with fresh youth and vigor."

Fearing that the cause of their holy Brother might be cast

aside if public veneration was paid to him before the Church pronounced on his life, the Fathers at Montesion had tenderly removed the sacred treasure of his body from the chapel of our Lady in 1656, and interred it beneath the floor of the sanctuary in the church. But the dampness of the place caused them to again move it, in 1722. In the presence of the Father Visitor, the rector of Montesion and the other members of the community, it was carried, in the old coffins in which it had been placed, to the little chamber where the Brother had died. There the two outer wooden boxes were opened, then the inner coffin, of lead. The remains of Brother Alonso Rodriguez were now exposed for the first time to the light of day. The flesh had disappeared, only the bones remained. They were covered with moisture, and in some parts, with fragments of the winding sheet in which they were originally placed. This first exhumation and examination showed the skeleton to be practically intact.

Two days later, on June 11, the treasure was laid in a new lead coffin, lined with green silk, and interred in a stone vault which had been made ready beneath the floor of the chamber. Further expulsions of the Fathers from the college caused them to be left untouched until 1823, when the community again returned.

In view of the approaching beatification of Brother Rodriguez, a final inspection of the sacred relics was made. The beatification ceremonies, were held on June 12, 1825, when, after the reading of the brief of beatification, the veil concealing a beautiful painting of Alonso was removed, and he was revealed to the great multitude in all his humility and simplicity, as he had been in life. At the close of the ceremonies, the Pontiff, accompanied by members of the Sacred College and prelates of the Papal Court, visited St. Peter's Basilica to venerate the new "Blessed" and to receive from the Father General of the Society of Jesus, Father Forte, a first-class relic, a piece of the bone of the beloved Lay Brother.

The remains of the Blessed Alonso were transferred to the magnificent new chapel at Montesion, which had long awaited their coming, on October 21 of that year.

In 1831 a petition was presented to the Sacred Congregation of Rites, asking for an inquiry into the two miracles proposed for the cause of canonization. One was the case of a young girl victim of smallpox who had been reduced to the point of death and who recovered perfect health immediately after she had asked that a Mass be said for her cure in honor of Blessed Alonso Rodriguez. The other was that of a Colletine nun, who also lay dying, with no hope for her recovery, and in such a physical condition that no human means could restore her, even a little. She asked the holy Brother to effect her cure, and he answered the prayer. She rose and joined her community in the religious exercises of her convent, completely well. This miracle was approved on February 4, 1871. The cause then rested until Pope Leo XIII ascended the throne of St. Peter. The final congregation on the cause was held in his presence on September 6, 1887. On January 15, 1888, the holy Lay Brother was solemnly canonized in St. Peter's Basilica, with two others of the Society of Jesus, Peter Claver, the disciple of Brother Alonso Rodriguez, missionary to the Negroes of South America, and John Berchmans, scholastic, also the seven founders of the Servite Order.

Segovia and Palma shared honors in the jubilation which greeted the canonization of their beloved Brother. But it was Palma which had the ineffable joy of possessing his sacred remains. They were removed from their resting place to be carried through the streets of the city which had known the tread of the Brother's feet for so many years, and enthroned in the cathedral. There throngs visited and honored them. They were then carried back to Montesion by another route, so that other thousands might share in the great privilege and triumph.

The relics of Saint Alonso Rodriguez were enclosed in a covering of wax, then clothed in a habit of rich black velvet.

On the head was placed a silver crown, having silver rays proceeding from it. They were then deposited in a sarcophagus, through whose glass panels they could be readily seen. Majorca gave of its famed polished jasper to provide a rich base for this casket. Its fluted columns of white marble support the dome which provides a canopy over the head of the Saint. There Saint Alonso Rodriguez rests, in the midst of those he loved and who loved him and honored him, the great model of Jesuit lay brothers the world over, of all lay brothers, faithful servitors of the servants of Christ.

Fortunately, the marvels which marked the religious life of the humble Brother caused those who lived with him to keep a careful record of his words and deeds. Fathers, scholastics and lay brothers who had lived with him at Montesion testified after his death as to his exalted virtues. Others who served as witnesses to his holiness were members of the nobility of Palma, among them a noble lady who as a child at Bellver Castle had witnessed the miracle of the doves flying about the head of Brother Rodriguez and lighting upon him, with no knowledge on his part that they were there.

The old monuments and landmarks of Palma remain practically the same as in the days of the saintly Brother. The Cathedral, with its flying pinnacles and buttresses, still stands beside the quay, and Bellver Castle crowns a wooded height above the old city.

At Montesion, on its little eminence overlooking the shimmering bay and the silent mountains, the Jesuit sons of St. Ignatius carry on their noble work for God and souls. Over the tomb of their Saint they keep jealous guard as they strive to extend the knowledge of his beautiful life throughout the world.

Many come to pray beside the tomb of the one-time wool merchant of Segovia, who exchanged the fine garments of a prosperous man of the world for the lowly habit of a lay brother in the Company of Jesus, and in the fulfillment of the most menial offices, rose to sanctity and the performance of miracles.